DC
ENTERTAINMENT™

May 2014

For decades DC Entertainment has been at the forefront of the graphic novel revolution, publishing the most acclaimed stories from the greatest talents in the industry. From Alan Moore and Dave Gibbons' WATCHMEN, to Scott Snyder and Greg Capullo's BATMAN VOL. 1: THE COURT OF OWLS, DC Comics, Vertigo and MAD have been reinforcing the graphic novel as not just a medium to entertain and excite, but also as one of popular culture's greatest art forms.

There's just one problem: where to begin?

Right here. With the DCE ESSENTIAL GRAPHIC NOVELS AND CHRONOLOGY catalog, we're presenting an easy entry point for all those who want to know exactly how to break into our rich backlist of titles.

For new readers, this catalog will be the perfect gateway through which to start exploring the breadth and depth of DC Entertainment's comprehensive library, from the earliest DC Comics superhero tales, to cutting-edge stories from Vertigo, to the irreverent humor of MAD. We realize how daunting it can be to look at a wall of graphic novels, but we hope to help guide readers to what we feel are the best entry points into not only our three imprints, but the comic book medium at large. For our dedicated fan base, this will be a refreshing look back at how our incredible talent has created the richest and most multilayered mythology in the world of comics.

In this new volume of our Essentials catalog, we've updated the listings with new releases, updated editions, a section for new initiatives such as Vertigo Defy and Digital-First publishing, as well as our backlist chronology with the newest that DC Comics, Vertigo and MAD have to offer.

Welcome to DC Entertainment.

Jim Lee	Dan DiDio
Co-Publisher	Co-Publisher

A Warner Bros Entertainment Company
4000 Warner Blvd Burbank CA 91522

Cover art by Terry Dodson and Rachel Dodson.

DC Comics, 1700 Broadway, New York, NY 10019
A Warner Bros. Entertainment Company.

Printed by Transcontinental Interglobe, Beauceville, QC, Canada. 5/1/13.
First Printing.

ISBN: 978-1-4012-5251-9

This label only applies to the text section.

TABLE OF CONTENTS

25 ESSENTIAL

GRAPHIC NOVELS

WATCHMEN

THE GREATEST GRAPHIC NOVEL OF ALL TIME

One of the most influential graphic novels of all time and a perennial bestseller, WATCHMEN is considered a gateway title to the entire graphic storytelling medium. Alan Moore and Dave Gibbons's seminal story is the benchmark against which all other graphic novels and comic books are judged.

A murder mystery-turned-nationwide conspiracy, WATCHMEN examines the lives of the eponymous superhero team as they seem to decay alongside the ever-darkening America around them. Rorschach, Nite Owl, the Silk Spectre, Dr. Manhattan and Ozymandias reunite to investigate who's behind a teammate's murder, but find that the truth may be even more grim than the world they seek to protect.

"A work of ruthless psychological realism, it's a landmark in the graphic novel medium. It would be a masterpiece in any." —*TIME Magazine*, *TIME Magazine*'s 100 best English-language novels since 1923

"Remarkable. The would-be heroes of WATCHMEN have staggeringly complex psychological profiles." —*The New York Times Book Review*

"Dark, violent and blackly funny, WATCHMEN is a comic book like no other…. [It is] the *Crime and Punishment* of graphic novels." —*London Times*

WATCHMEN

American Edition: Writer: Alan Moore | Artist: Dave Gibbons | ISBN: 978-1-4012-4525-2 | Diamond Code: FEB140265 | Price: $19.99 | Format: TP

International Edition: Writer: Alan Moore | Artist: Dave Gibbons | ISBN: 978-1-4012-4819-2 | Diamond Code: FEB140266 | Price: $19.99 | Format: TP

BATMAN:
THE DARK KNIGHT RETURNS
THE GREATEST BATMAN STORY EVER TOLD

Ten years after an aging Batman has retired, Gotham City has sunk deeper into decadence and lawlessness. Now, when his city needs him most, the Dark Knight returns in a blaze of glory. Joined by Carrie Kelly, a teenage female Robin, Batman must take back the streets.

But for a man his age, a return to a life of crime-fighting is not easy. After facing off against two of his greatest enemies, the Joker and Two-Face, a haggard Batman finds himself in mortal combat with his former ally, Superman, in a battle that only one of them will survive.

Hailed as a comics masterpiece, THE DARK KNIGHT RETURNS is Frank Miller's (*300* and *Sin City*) reinvention of Gotham's legendary protector. It remains one of the most influential stories ever told in comics, and is a book cited by the filmmakers as an inspiration for the recent blockbuster Batman movies.

"Groundbreaking." —*USA Today*

"It's film noir in cartoon panels." —*Vanity Fair*

"Changed the course of comics." —*Rolling Stone*

"Revisionist pop epic." —*SPIN*

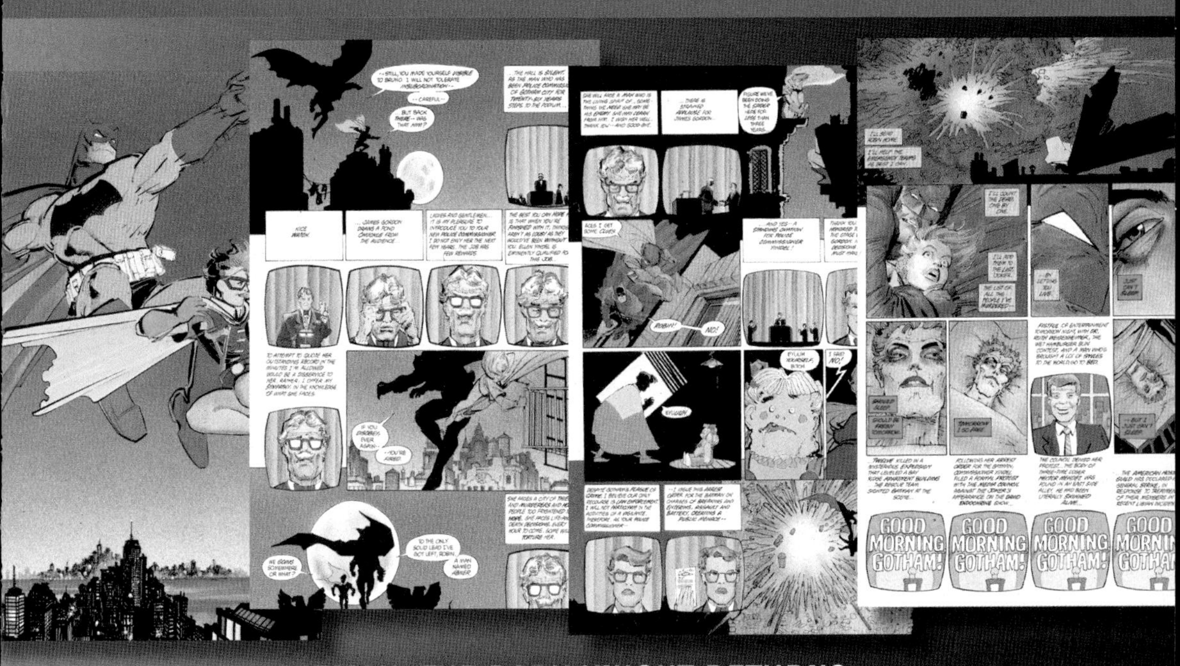

BATMAN: THE DARK KNIGHT RETURNS

Writer: Frank Miller | Artist: Frank Miller | ISBN: 978-1-5638-9342-1 | Diamond Code: NOV118095 | Price: $19.99 | Format: TP

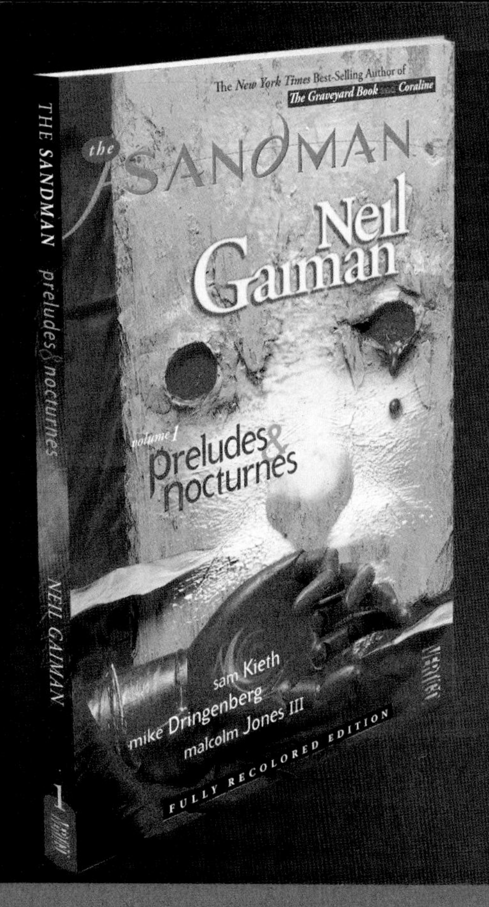

THE SANDMAN

VOL.1: PRELUDES & NOCTURNES

THE FIRST VOLUME OF THE DEFINITIVE VERTIGO SERIES BY THE LEGENDARY NEIL GAIMAN

The *New York Times* best-selling author Neil Gaiman's transcendent series THE SANDMAN is often labeled as not only the definitive Vertigo title, but also as one of the finest achievements in graphic storytelling. Gaiman created an unforgettable tale of the forces that exist beyond life and death by weaving ancient mythology, folklore and fairy tales with his own distinct narrative vision.

In THE SANDMAN VOLUME 1: PRELUDES & NOCTURNES, an occultist attempting to capture Death to bargain for eternal life traps her younger brother Dream instead. After his seventy-year imprisonment and eventual escape, Dream, also known as Morpheus, goes on a quest for his lost objects of power to reclaim his power.

"THE SANDMAN just might be the smartest comic book ever written." —*USA Today*

"Neil Gaiman's long-running series made cool comics fantastical and fantastical comics cool. THE SANDMAN is a modern myth, as well as a précis on why the stories we tell matter so much." —*Playboy*

"The greatest epic in the history of comic books." —*Los Angeles Times Magazine*

THE SANDMAN VOL. 1: PRELUDES & NOCTURNES

Writer: Neil Gaiman | Artists: Sam Kieth, Malcolm Jones III, Mike Dringenberg | ISBN: 978-1-4012-2575-9 | Diamond Code: JUL100259 | Price: $19.99 | Format: TP

FOR MATURE READERS

BATMAN:
YEAR ONE
THE TIMELESS ORIGIN STORY OF THE CAPED CRUSADER

In 1986, Frank Miller and David Mazzucchelli produced this groundbreaking reinterpretation of the origin of Batman—who he is, and how he came to be. Sometimes careless and naive, this Dark Knight is far from the flawless vigilante he is today. In his first year on the job, Batman feels his way in a Gotham City far darker than when he left it. His solemn vow to extinguish the town's criminal element is only half the battle; along with Lieutenant James Gordon, the Dark Knight must also fight a police force more corrupt than the scum in the streets.

BATMAN: YEAR ONE stands alongside BATMAN: THE DARK KNIGHT RETURNS on the mantle of greatest Batman graphic novels of all time. Timeless in its appeal, Frank Miller and David Mazzucchelli's masterpiece would stand apart from the crowded comics field even today.

"It's not only one of the most important comics ever written, it's also among the best." —*IGN*

"There's never been storytelling quite like this. It took someone who views comics as an art to create it." —*Washington Post*

"This is a story no true Batman fan should be able to resist." —*School Library Journal*

BATMAN: YEAR ONE

Writer: Frank Miller | Artist: David Mazzucchelli | ISBN: 978-1-4012-0752-6 | Diamond Code: OCT060163 | Price: $14.99 | Format: TP

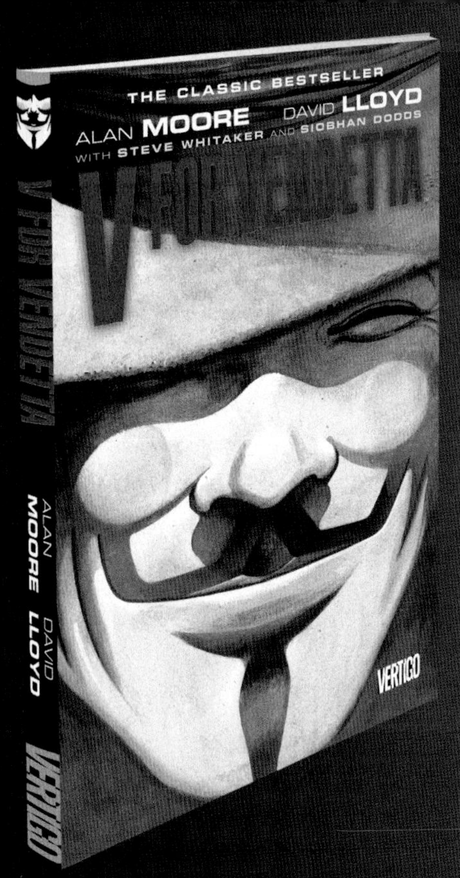

V FOR VENDETTA

A DARK PORTRAIT OF OPPRESSION AND RESISTANCE SET AGAINST THE BACKDROP OF DYSTOPIAN FUTURE ENGLAND

A visionary graphic novel that defines sophisticated storytelling, Alan Moore's best-selling V FOR VENDETTA is a terrifying portrait of totalitarianism and resistance, superbly illustrated by artist David Lloyd.

Set in a futurist totalitarian England, a country without freedom or faith, a mysterious man in a white porcelain mask strikes back against the oppressive overlords on behalf of the voiceless. This powerful story detailing the loss and fight for individuality has become a cultural touchstone and an enduring allegory for current events.

"Dark, gripping storytelling." —*Entertainment Weekly*

"Densely-packed, thematically vibrant and philosophically challenging." —*Scripps Howard News Service*

"Alan Moore has helped redefine the medium several times over." —*The Onion/A.V. Club*

V FOR VENDETTA

Writer: Alan Moore | Artist: David Lloyd | ISBN: 978-1-4012-0841-7 | Diamond Code: SEP088030 | Price: $19.99 | Format: TP

FOR MATURE READERS

SAGA OF THE SWAMP THING BOOK ONE

THE GROUNDBREAKING TITLE THAT LAUNCHED ALAN MOORE INTO COMICS SUPER-STARDOM

FROM THE AWARD-WINNING WRITER OF WATCHMEN
ALAN MOORE
SAGA OF THE SWAMP THING
BOOK ONE
STEPHEN BISSETTE
JOHN TOTLEBEN
VERTIGO

Before tackling WATCHMEN, Alan Moore made his debut in the U.S. comic book industry with the revitalization of the horror comic book THE SWAMP THING. His deconstruction of the classic monster stretched the creative boundaries of the medium and became one of the most spectacular series in industry history.

SAGA OF THE SWAMP THING came to explore modern-day issues against a backdrop of the macabre. With a host of some of the genre's greatest artists, Alan Moore's first masterpiece for DC/Vertigo serves as stunning commentary on environmental, political and social issues, unflinching in its relevance.

"Hyper intelligent, emotionally potent, and yes, fun. A." —*Entertainment Weekly*

"A cerebral meditation on the state of the American soul." —NPR

"Another of the true classics of the genre." —*IGN*

SAGA OF THE SWAMP THING BOOK ONE

Writer: Alan Moore | Artist: Stephen Bissette | ISBN: 978-1-4012-2083-9 | Diamond Code: JAN120343 | Price: $19.99 | Format: TP

FOR MATURE READERS

FABLES VOL. 1: LEGENDS IN EXILE

FOLKLORE COMES TO LIFE AS THESE REAL-LIFE FAIRY TALE CHARACTERS ARE EXILED IN MODERN-DAY NEW YORK

No longer just children's tales, writer and creator Bill Willingham has created a new world for these beloved fables ... one that exists within our own.

When a savage creature known only as the Adversary conquered the homeland of legends and myth, all of the infamous inhabitants of folklore were forced into exile. Disguised among the normal citizens of modern-day New York, these magical characters created their own secret society called Fabletown. But when Snow White's party-girl sister, Rose Red, is apparently murdered it us up to Bigby, the reformed Big Bad Wolf and Fabletown's sheriff, to find the killer.

FABLES VOLUME 1: LEGENDS IN EXILE is the critically acclaimed, best-selling first chapter OF one of Vertigo's great staple series.

"[A] wonderfully twisted concept." —*Washington Post*

"An epic, beautifully written story." —*The Onion*

"Great fun." —*Booklist*

FABLES VOL. 1: LEGENDS IN EXILE

Writer: Bill Willingham | Artists: Lan Medina & others | ISBN: 978-1-4012-3755-4 | Diamond Code: FEB120285 | Price: $12.99 | Format: TP

FOR MATURE READERS

BATMAN: THE KILLING JOKE THE DELUXE EDITION

ALAN MOORE'S UNFORGETTABLE MEDITATION ON THE RAZOR-THIN LINE BETWEEN SANITY AND INSANITY, HEROISM AND VILLAINY, COMEDY AND TRAGEDY

In this groundbreaking work, Moore weaves together a twisted tale of insanity and human perseverance featuring Batman's greatest foe, the Joker.

Looking to prove that any man can be pushed past his breaking point into madness, the Joker attempts to drive Commissioner Gordon insane. Refusing to give up even after suffering a tremendous personal tragedy, Gordon struggles to maintain his sanity with the help of Batman in a desperate effort to best the madman.

With art by one of comics' best illustrators in Brian Bolland, BATMAN: THE KILLING JOKE is a chilling introspection into the mind of fiction's most notorious villain.

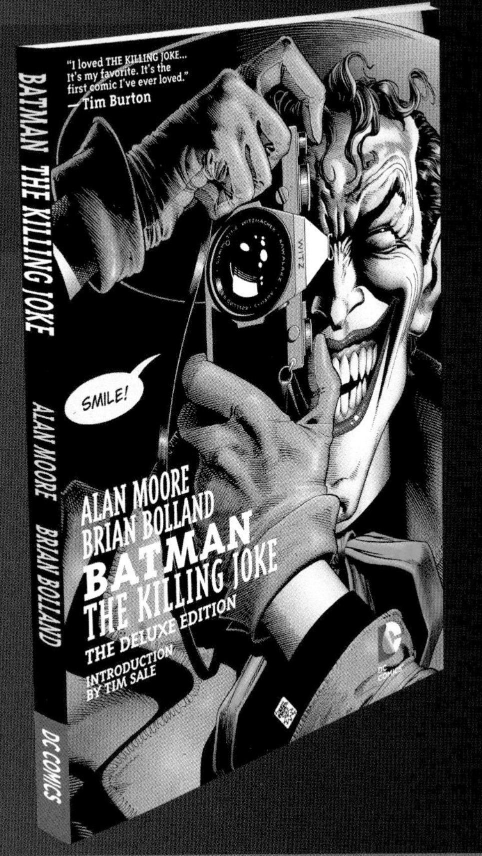

"Easily the greatest Joker story ever told, BATMAN: THE KILLING JOKE is also one of Alan Moore's finest works. If you've read it before, go back and read it again. You owe it to yourself." —*IGN*

"A genuinely chilling portrayal of Batman's greatest foe." —*Booklist*

"I loved THE KILLING JOKE. It's my favorite. It's the first comic I ever loved." —Tim Burton

BATMAN: THE KILLING JOKE: THE DELUXE EDITION

Writer: Alan Moore | Artist: Brian Bolland | ISBN: 978-1-4012-1667-2 | Diamond Code: NOV070226 | Price: $17.99 | Format: HC

Y: THE LAST MAN

VOL. 1: UNMANNED

WHAT WOULD YOU DO IF YOU WERE THE LAST MAN ON EARTH?

Y: THE LAST MAN is that rare example of a page-turner that is all at once humorous, socially relevant and endlessly surprising.

Written by Brian K. Vaughan (LOST, PRIDE OF BAGHDAD, EX MACHINA) and with art by Pia Guerra, this is the saga of Yorick Brown, the only human survivor of a planet-wide plague that instantly kills every mammal possessing a Y chromosome. Accompanied by a mysterious government agent, a brilliant young geneticist and his pet monkey, Ampersand, Yorick travels the world in search of his lost love and the answer to why he's the last man on Earth.

"Funny and scary. An unbelievable critique of society. A+." —*Washington Post*

"The best graphic novel I've ever read." —Stephen King

"This year's best movie is a comic book." —"All Things Considered," National Public Radio

Y: THE LAST MAN VOL. 1: UNMANNED

Writer: Brian K. Vaughan | Artist: Pia Guerra | ISBN: 978-1-5638-9980-5 | Diamond Code: DEC108152 | Price: $14.99 | Format: TP

FOR MATURE READERS

ALL-STAR SUPERMAN

THE CRITICALLY ACCLAIMED, GENRE-BENDING SERIES THAT HARKENS BACK TO THE GOLDEN AGE OF THE MAN OF STEEL

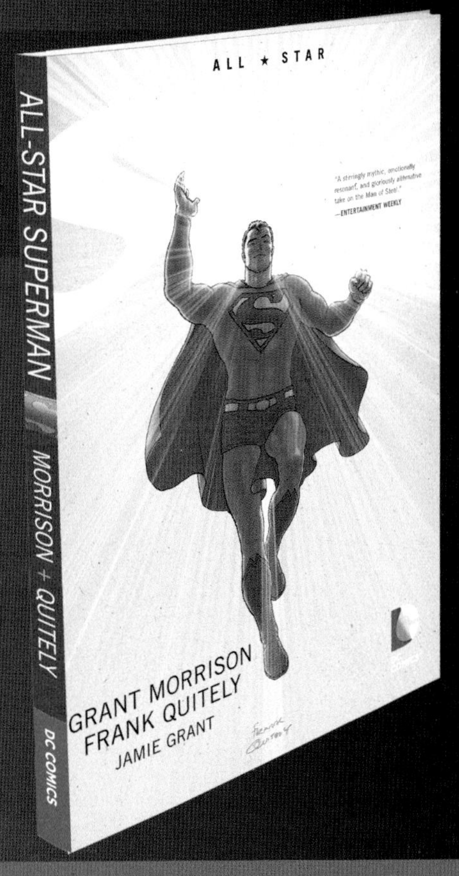

The Underverse ruled by Bizarros. The time-eating Chronovore. Jimmy Olsen, superhero?

Nothing is impossible in ALL-STAR SUPERMAN.

The unstoppable creative team of writer Grant Morrison and artist Frank Quitely (WE3, FLEX MENTALLO, JLA: EARTH 2) join forces once more to take Superman back to basics. In an emotionally and visually stunning graphic novel harkening back to a Golden Age of comics, ALL-STAR SUPERMAN creates a new, and at the same time familiar, take on the World's First Superhero.

"Maniacally brilliant." —*The New York Times*

"A stirringly mythic, emotionally resonant, and gloriously alternative take on the Man of Steel." —*Entertainment Weekly*

"Taking the Man of Steel back to his roots and into the future at the same time, ALL-STAR SUPERMAN is exciting, bold and supercool … all the makings of a classic." —*Variety*

ALL-STAR SUPERMAN

Writer: Grant Morrison | Artist: Frank Quitely | ISBN: 978-1-4012-3205-4 | Diamond Code: JUL110247 | Price: $29.99 | Format: TP

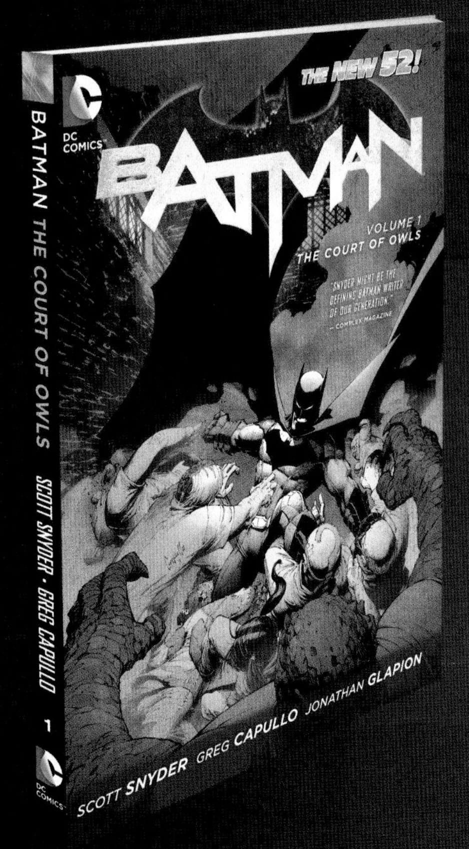

BATMAN

VOL. 1: THE COURT OF OWLS

A NEW ERA FOR THE DARK KNIGHT AND GOTHAM CITY BEGINS HERE IN THIS #1 *NEW YORK TIMES* BESTSELLER!

Batman has heard tales of Gotham City's Court of Owls: That the members of this powerful cabal are the true rulers of Gotham. The Dark Knight dismissed the stories as rumors and old wives' tales. Gotham was his city. Until now.

A brutal assassin is sinking his razor-sharp talons into the city's best and brightest, as well as its most dangerous and deadly. If the dark legends are true, his masters are more powerful predators than the Batman could ever imagine.

Writer Scott Snyder and artist Greg Capullo have created a graphic novel that pays respect to 75 years of the Dark Knight's mythology, and yet generates a take on Batman that's wholly unique and epic in scale. A part of DC Comics–The New 52, BATMAN VOL. 1: THE COURT OF OWLS has quickly ascended to the status of "modern classic."

"[Writer Scott Snyder] pulls from the oldest aspects of the Batman myth, combines it with sinister comic elements from the series' best period, and gives the whole thing a terrific forward-spin by setting up an honest-to-gosh mystery for Batman to solve." —*Entertainment Weekly*

"A stunning debut.... Snyder knows these characters, sets up an intriguing mystery, and delivers some action that Capullo realizes stunningly. This is definitely in the top rank of the revamp." —*The Onion/A.V. Club*

BATMAN VOL. 1: THE COURT OF OWLS

Writer: Scott Snyder | Artist: Greg Capullo | ISBN: 978-1-4012-3542-0 | Diamond Code: DEC120323 | Price: $16.99 | Format: TP

KINGDOM COME

OLD AND NEW ERAS OF SUPERHEROES ARE PITTED AGAINST EACH OTHER IN THIS EPIC GRAPHIC NOVEL

Winner of five Eisner and Harvey Awards, KINGDOM COME is the best-selling graphic novel form acclaimed writer Mark Waid and superstar painter Alex Ross.

Set in the not so distant future, the DC Universe is spinning inexorably out of control. The new generation of heroes has lost their moral compass, becoming just as reckless and violent as the villains they fight. The previous regime of heroes—the Justice League—returns under the most dire of circumstances, setting up a battle of the old guard against these uncompromising protectors in a battle that will define what heroism truly is.

"Waid's charged dialogue and Ross' stunning visual realism expose the genius, pride, fears and foibles of DC's heroes and villains." —*Washington Post*

"No library should be without some edition of this book." —*Library Journal*

"Wagnerian. Credit Mark Waid's script for keeping the mood dark and morally muddled, but it's Alex Ross's thousand-plus watercolor panels (reproduced in captivating detail) that propel these scenes of Revelation-style apocalypse and reborn hope." —*Village Voice*

KINGDOM COME

Writer: Mark Waid | Artist: Alex Ross | ISBN: 978-1-4012-2034-1 | Diamond Code: SEP138294 | Price: $19.99 | Format: TP

BATMAN:
THE LONG HALLOWEEN

A CLASSIC BATMAN MURDER MYSTERY BY THE ACCLAIMED CREATIVE TEAM OF JEPH LOEB AND TIM SALE

Set just after Batman's first year in Gotham City, the Dark Knight finds himself working alongside District Attorney Harvey Dent and Lieutenant James Gordon, trying to vanquish the criminal element. However, a serial killer known only as Holiday has been killing friend and foe each month. Batman races against the calendar trying to discover the assassin's identity, fighting the entirety of Gotham's rogues' gallery along the way.

The magnificent creative team of Jeph Loeb and Tim Sale reach their apex in BATMAN: THE LONG HALLOWEEN, propelling the graphic novel to its place amongst comics' finest murder mystery stories.

"THE LONG HALLOWEEN stretches beyond the normal boundaries of comics to create a legendary story of one man's crusade against an insane world."—*IGN*

"THE LONG HALLOWEEN is more than a comic book. It's an epic tragedy."
—Christopher Nolan (director of *Batman Begins, The Dark Knight* and *The Dark Knight Rises*)

BATMAN: THE LONG HALLOWEEN

Writer: Jeph Loeb | Artist: Tim Sale | ISBN: 978-1-4012-3259-7 | Diamond Code: JUL110251 | Price: $24.99 | Format: TP

JUSTICE LEAGUE
VOL. 1: ORIGIN

IN THE NEW 52'S FLAGSHIP TITLE, GEOFF JOHNS AND JIM LEE UNITE FOR THE FIRST TIME TO LAUNCH THE BOLD NEW BEGINNING OF THE DC UNIVERSE'S PREMIER SUPER TEAM!

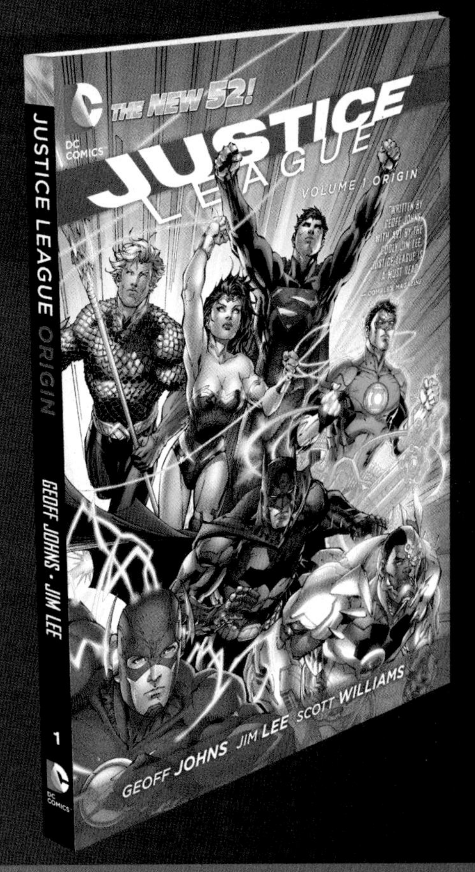

It's the dawn of a new age of superheroes, frightening to the world at large. Superman. Batman. The Flash. Wonder Woman. Green Lantern. Aquaman. Cyborg. Though young and inexperienced, brash and overconfident, each one alone is a powerful force in the battle of good against evil. Together, they may be the only thing on Earth that can stop the alien warlord Darkseid from claiming our planet as his own. Together they will become the Justice League!

The superstar creative team of Geoff Johns and Jim Lee come together to relaunch the most iconic team in comics with this accessible, game-changing graphic novel.

"A must-read." —*Complex Magazine*

"Writer Geoff Johns and artist Jim Lee toss you–and their heroes–into the action from the very start and don't put on the brakes. DC's über-creative team craft an inviting world for those who are trying out a comic for the first time." —*USA Today*

"Welcoming to new fans looking to get into superhero comics for the first time and old fans who gave up on the funny-books long ago." —*MTV Geek!*

JUSTICE LEAGUE VOL. 1: ORIGIN

Writer: Geoff Johns | Artist: Jim Lee | ISBN: 978-1-4012-3788-2 | Diamond Code: OCT120252 | Price: $16.99 | Format: TP

THE LEAGUE OF EXTRAORDINARY GENTLEMEN VOL. 1

PROMINENT FIGURES FROM NINETEENTH-CENTURY LITERATURE BAND TOGETHER IN ALAN MOORE'S AWARD-WINNING GRAPHIC NOVEL

London, 1898. The Victorian Era draws to a close and the twentieth century approaches. It is a time of great change and stagnation, a period of chaste order and ignoble chaos. It is an era in need of champions. A League.

In this amazingly imaginative graphic novel from Alan Moore and Kevin O'Neill, the most popular turn-of-the-century literary figures are brought together to face any and all threats coming to Britain. Allan Quartermain, Mina Murray, Dr. Henry Jekyll and Edward Hyde, Captain Nemo and Hawley Griffin, the Invisible Man, form the League of Extraordinary Gentlemen.

"A great graphic novel. Indeed extraordinary." —*Time Magazine*

"Moore has combined his love of nineteenth century literature with an imaginative mastery of its twentieth century corollary, the superhero comic book." —*Publishers Weekly*

"Inventive and suspenseful." —*Library Journal*

THE LEAGUE OF EXTRAORDINARY GENTLEMEN VOL. 1

Writer: Alan Moore | Artist: Kevin O'Neill | ISBN: 978-1-5638-9858-7 | Diamond Code: MAY118167 | Price: $16.99 | Format: TP

FOR MATURE READERS

BATMAN:
EARTH ONE

GEOFF JOHNS REIMAGINES THE DARK KNIGHT'S ORIGIN STORY IN THIS #1 *NEW YORK TIMES* BESTSELLER

Batman is not a hero. He is just a man. Fallible, vulnerable and angry.

In Gotham City where friend and foe are indistinguishable, Bruce Wayne's path toward becoming the Dark Knight is riddled with more obstacles than ever before. Focused on punishing his parents' true killer, and the corrupt police who allowed them to go free, Bruce Wayne's thirst for vengeance fuels his mad crusade and no one, not even Alfred, can stop him.

In this #1 *New York Times* bestseller, writer Geoff Johns and artist Gary Frank reimagine a new mythology for the Dark Knight, where the familiar is no longer the expected in this original graphic novel.

"Just when you thought there couldn't possibly be a fresh take on Batman, along come Johns & Frank to prove you extraordinarily wrong. Original, surprising and emotional, BATMAN: EARTH ONE is a must-read." —Damon Lindelof (Co-creator and Executive Producer of *Lost*)

"This isn't just about capes and tights. This is stuff that, like the best of fiction, goes beyond the parameters of its particular genre." —*MTV Geek!*

"BATMAN: EARTH ONE will knock your socks off." —*Huffington Post*

BATMAN: EARTH ONE

Writer: Geoff Johns | Artist: Gary Frank | ISBN: 978-1-4012-3208-5 | Diamond Code: MAR120234 | Price: $22.99 | Format: HC

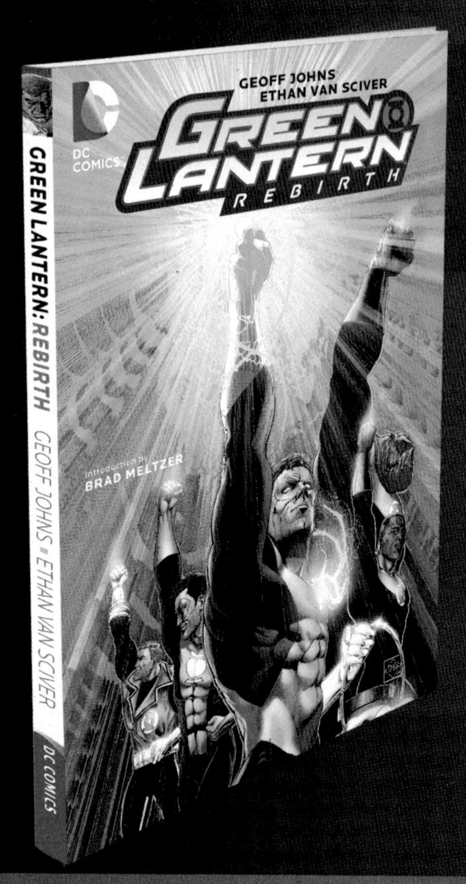

GREEN LANTERN: REBIRTH

REINTRODUCING THE ICONIC HERO FOR A NEW GENERATION

Hal Jordan was the greatest Green Lantern of them all, until his shocking fall from grace. After years away, the battle for Emerald Warrior's soul has begun in earnest, with an alien evil threatening to consume the galaxy. As the other heroes on Earth (and beyond) attempt to save the Earth, several strive to bring back their fallen friend into the land of the living.

GREEN LANTERN: REBIRTH is the best-selling graphic novel that relaunches one of the DC Comics' greatest heroes from writer Geoff Johns and artist Ethan Van Sciver.

"Readers will thrill at seeing one of the DC Universe's best mythologies begin to return to its former glory." —*Washington Post*

"This is comic book storytelling at its absolute finest." —*IGN*

"An epic blockbuster." —*CNN*

GREEN LANTERN: REBIRTH

Writer: Geoff Johns | Artist: Ethan Van Sciver | ISBN: 978-1-4012-2755-5 | Diamond Code: FEB100185 | Price: $14.99 | Format: TP

AMERICAN VAMPIRE
VOL. 1

SCOTT SNYDER AND STEPHEN KING SET FIRE TO THE HORROR GENRE WITH A VISIONARY TAKE ON ONE OF POP CULTURE'S MOST INFAMOUS MONSTERS

Everything you know about vampires has changed. The first bloodsucker conceived on American soil, Skinner Sweet, is not your usual creature of the night. Stronger, fiercer, and powered by the sun, he is the first of a new breed: the American Vampire.

Comics superstar Scott Snyder and the master of horror Stephen King join forces for one of Vertigo's strongest—and most original—series ever.

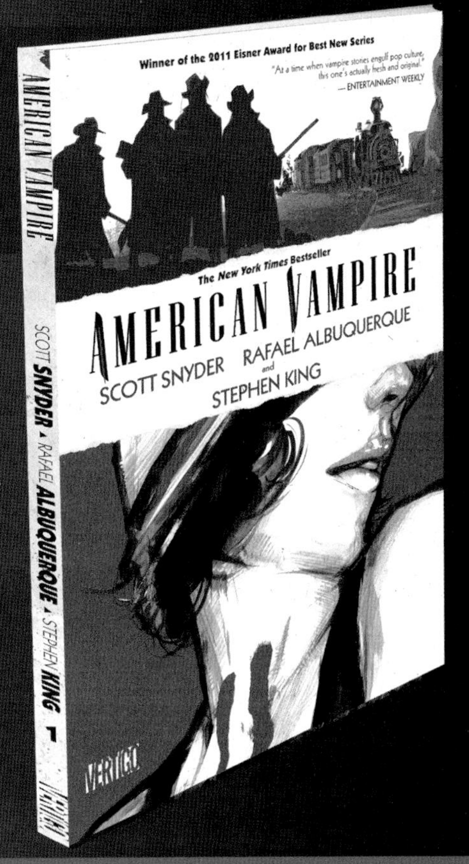

"A rich, textured romp through vampire Americana, in such a fun way as to suggest the possibilities of this vehicle are as endless as the lives of the undead." —*IGN*

"Looking for a vampire story with some real bite? Then, boys and girls, Scott Snyder has a comic book for you." —*USA Weekend*

AMERICAN VAMPIRE VOL. 1

Writers: Scott Snyder & Stephen King | Artist: Rafael Albuquerque | ISBN: 978-1-4012-2974-0 | Diamond Code: JUL110284 | Price: $19.99 | Format: TP

FOR MATURE READERS

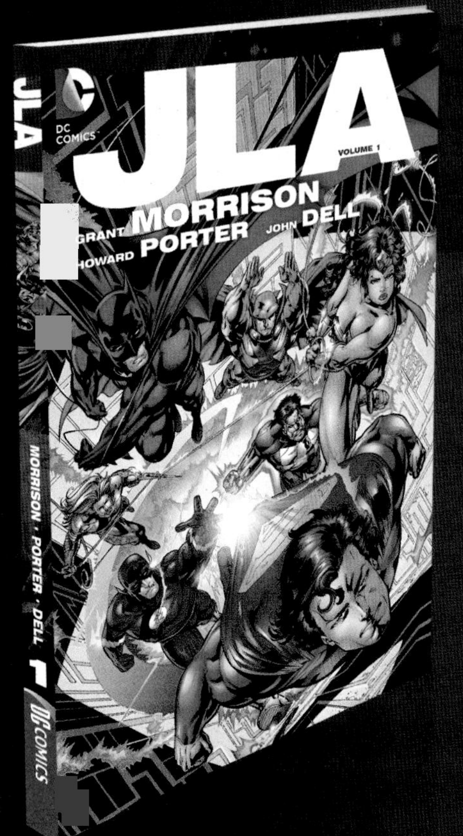

JLA VOL. 1

GRANT MORRISON RELAUNCHES THE GREATEST TEAM IN THE DC UNIVERSE WITH THE WORLD'S MOST POWERFUL HEROES

Grant Morrison relaunches the greatest team in the DC Universe–returning the powerhouse lineup of Superman, Batman, Wonder Woman, the Flash, Green Lantern, Aquaman and Martian Manhunter!

Renegade angels, alien invaders and robot infiltrators. Sometimes, even the World's Greatest Superheroes face threats too great for one man ... or woman. DC's pantheon of champions–Superman, Batman, Wonder Woman, The Flash, Green Lantern, Aquaman, and Martian Manhunter–are finally united as the JLA.

Critically acclaimed writer Grant Morrison ushers in a brand new era for DC's finest in this graphic novel that changed the dynamics of the 90s superhero.

"[Grant Morrison is] comics' high shaman." —*Washington Post*

"Morrison's JLA is overloaded with cool moments, cooler lines, and that ever-present vibe of greatness we've come to expect from superhero team books. To this day fans are still citing this work as the 'model' for the JLA franchise." —*Newsarama*

JLA VOL. 1

Writer: Grant Morrison | Artists: Howard Porter & Oscar Jimenez | ISBN: 978-1-4012-3314-3 | Diamond Code: JUN110276 | Price: $19.99 | Format: TP

FINAL CRISIS

GRANT MORRISON TAKES THE DC UNIVERSE ON A BATTLE THROUGH THE MULTIVERSE THAT WILL LEAVE BOTH HERO AND VILLAIN CHANGED FOREVER!

What happens when evil wins? That's the devastating question Superman, Batman, and the Justice League must face when Darkseid and his invading hordes win the war between light and dark. The fate of the universe is in jeopardy, and in order to see tomorrow, one of the world's greatest superheroes will pay the ultimate price.

Written by superstar creator Grant Morrison with stellar art from J.G. Jones, Carlos Pacheco and Doug Mahnke, this graphic novel is one of the most ambitious works in DC Comics history.

"Epic." —*Washington Post*

"The fertile mind of writer Grant Morrison...this [is] the event to trump all events." —*Entertainment Weekly*

"Beautiful." —*Publishers Weekly*

FINAL CRISIS

Writer: Grant Morrison | Artists: J.G. Jones, Doug Mahnke & Carlos Pacheco | ISBN: 978-1-4012-4517-7 | Diamond Code: JAN140352 | Price: $19.99 | Format: TP

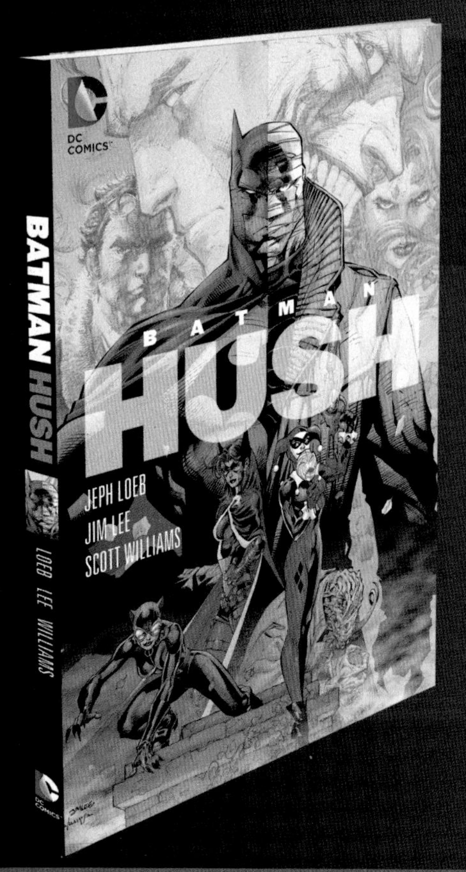

BATMAN: HUSH

BATMAN STALKS A DEADLY VILLAIN WHO SEEMS TO KNOW MORE ABOUT THE DARK KNIGHT THAN ANYONE—HUSH!

Gotham City's worst criminals have emerged to throw Batman's life into utter chaos. However, these villains–Joker, Riddler, Ra's al Ghul, Clayface and others–are a part of a much more elaborate, sinister scheme to destroy the Dark Knight once and for all. Pushed past his breaking point, Batman will need to use more than the world's greatest detective skills to uncover the true mastermind behind this murderous plot before those closest to Bruce Wayne suffer the consequences.

In this truly unforgettable story by two of comics' top talents, writer Jeph Loeb and DC Co-Publisher Jim Lee present the Caped Crusader's most personal case yet.

"It's beautiful stuff. Catwoman has rarely looked so seductive, nor has Batman's heroic but fearsome image often been used so well. [HUSH] make[s] readers look at Batman and his colleagues with a fresh, enthusiastic eye." —*Publishers Weekly*

"Jim Lee's art, which just might be his best work in his time at DC Comics." —*IGN*

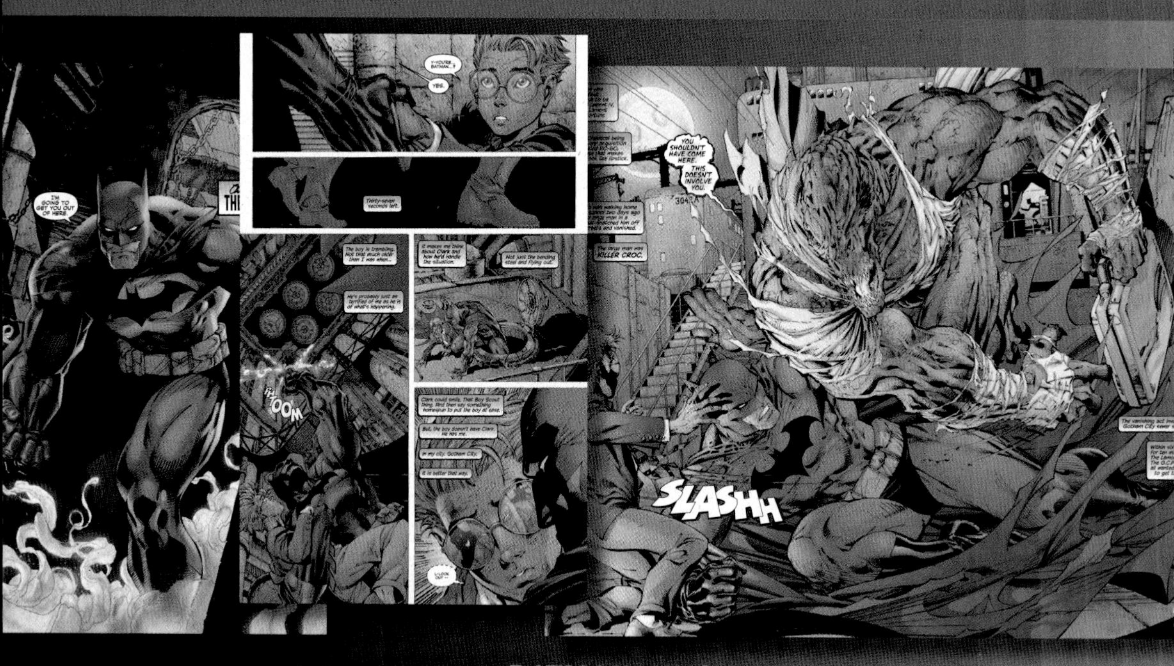

BATMAN: HUSH

Writer: Jeph Loeb | Artist: Jim Lee | ISBN: 978-1-4012-2317-5 | Diamond Code: MAY090178 | Price: $24.99 | Format: TP

IDENTITY CRISIS

UNCOVER THE DC UNIVERSE'S DEADLIEST SECRET IN THIS ACCLAIMED STORY FROM #1 *NEW YORK TIMES* BEST-SELLING NOVELIST BRAD MELTZER

After a grisly murder rocks the DC Universe, the entire superhero community searches for the killer. But before the mystery is solved, a number of long-buried secrets will threaten to divide the Justice League.

New York Times best-selling novelist Brad Meltzer teams with critically acclaimed artist Rags Morales to unravel one of the most intimate and heartbreaking graphic novels ever.

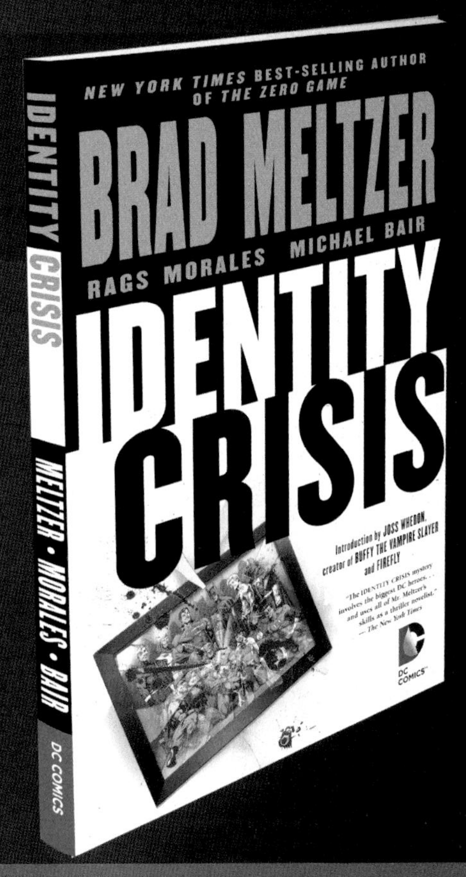

"The IDENTITY CRISIS mystery involves the biggest DC heroes and will use all of Mr. Meltzer's skills as a thriller novelist." —*The New York Times*

"Meltzer deftly handles this foray into the question of how far the 'good guys' can go in questioning a 'bad guy.' One hopes that Meltzer enjoyed his stay in the comic book world enough to make a trip back someday." —*Chicago Sun-Times*

"Meltzer shows that even superheroes have reasons to be afraid." —*SPIN*

IDENTITY CRISIS

Writer: Brad Meltzer | Artist: Rags Morales | ISBN: 978-1-4012-0458-7 | Diamond Code: AUG118125 | Price: $17.99 | Format: TP

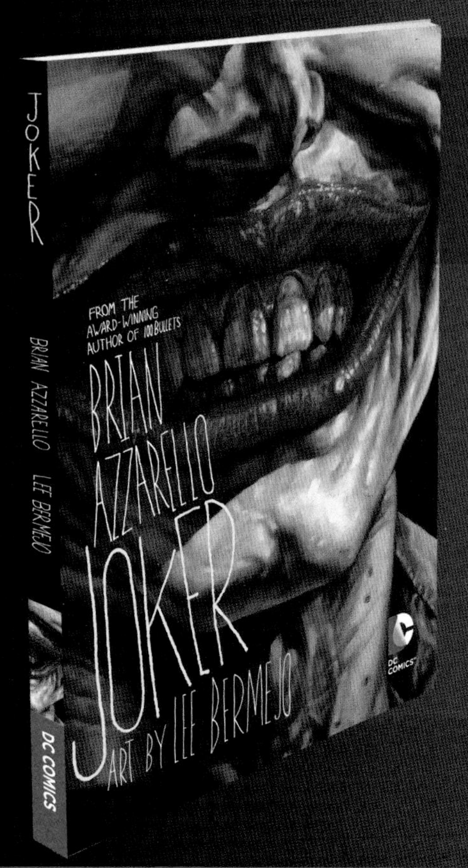

JOKER

BRIAN AZZARELLO AND LEE BERMEJO'S ORIGINAL GRAPHIC NOVEL MASTERPIECE TRACES THE MOST VILE, DANGEROUS AND UNPREDICTABLE INMATE OF ARKHAM—THE JOKER!

The Joker has been mysteriously released from Arkham Asylum, and he's not too happy about what's happened to his town while he's been away. What follows is a harrowing night of revenge, murder and manic crime, as he brutally takes back his stolen assets from the Penguin, Riddler, Two-Face, Killer Croc, and, of course, the Batman.

Brian Azzarello brings all the visceral intensity and criminal insight to JOKER that has made his Vertigo graphic novel series 100 BULLETS one of the most critically acclaimed and award-winning comic series of this generation. With gorgeous illustrations by one of the industry's very best in Lee Bermejo, Batman's greatest foe takes center stage in this true crime noir novel–a harrowing journey into a city of rain-soaked streets, dirty sheets and nothing but bad choices.

"Disturbing, violent, oddly psychological and insanely wonderful." —*USA Today*

"A literary achievement that takes its place right alongside Alan Moore's BATMAN: THE KILLING JOKE." —*IGN*

"If you liked THE DARK KNIGHT, JOKER is a must-have for your bookshelf." —*MTV.com*

JOKER

Writer: Brian Azzarello | Artist: Lee Bermejo | ISBN: 978-1-4012-1581-1 | Diamond Code: JUL080124 | Price: $19.99 | Format: HC

WONDER WOMAN
VOL. 1: BLOOD

CRITICALLY ACCLAIMED WRITER BRIAN AZZARELLO TEAMS WITH CLIFF CHIANG AND TONY AKINS TO CREATE A NEW MYTHOLOGY FOR THE AMAZONIAN WARRIOR

Experience a bold new beginning of the iconic character in WONDER WOMAN VOLUME 1: BLOOD in this critically acclaimed and best-selling series!

Wonder Woman's world is shattered when a secret her mother Hippolyta, queen of the Amazons, kept all her life is revealed: Diana is not clay brought to life, but is in fact the child of Zeus! In this reimagining of Diana's history, superheroics and mythology seamlessly blend as Brian Azzarello (JOKER, 100 BULLETS) creates a new direction for one of the world's best known heroes. With stunning art by Cliff Chiang and Tony Akins, Wonder Woman has never looked better.

"Beautifully illustrated and brings a fresh, fascinating and fun take to the Amazon Princess and her world." —*IGN*

"It's a different direction for Wonder Woman, but one still steeped in mythology ... great things from Azzarello and Chiang." —*The Onion/A.V. Club*

"Azzarello is ... rebuilding the mythology of Wonder Woman." —*Maxim*

WONDER WOMAN VOLUME 1: BLOOD

Writer: Brian Azzarello | Artist: Cliff Chiang & Tony Akins | ISBN: 978-1-4012-3562-8 | Diamond Code: OCT120256 | Price: $14.99 | Format: TP

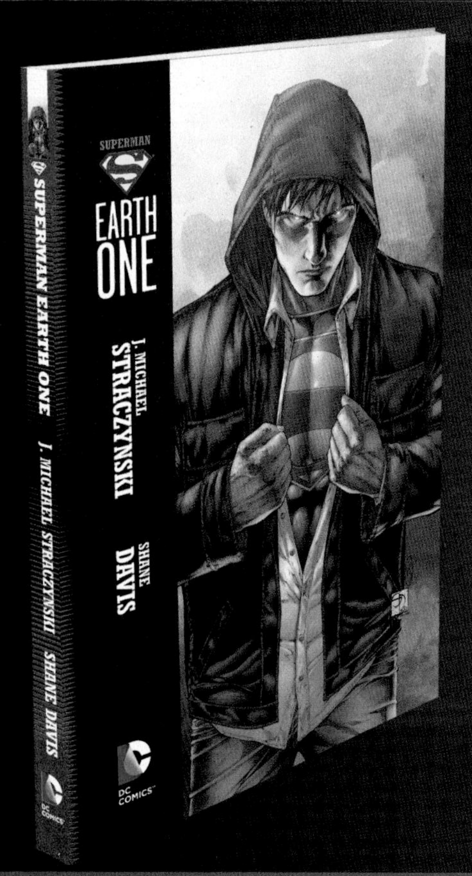

SUPERMAN: EARTH ONE VOL. 1

THE #1 *NEW YORK TIMES* BEST-SELLING ORIGINAL GRAPHIC NOVEL THAT REIMAGINES SUPERMAN AS A BROODING, RELUCTANT HERO IN MODERN-DAY METROPOLIS

Clark Kent is different. He can fly. He can see through walls, burn objects with his gaze. He is a man amongst mortals. But he is alone. Like most twenty-year-olds, he doesn't know what he wants to do with his life. After all, when you can do anything, the sky is the limit. But when the skies darken with ships from distant planets and the existence of Earth itself is threatened, Clark, must make the most important decision of his life: To reveal himself to the world, or let everything die around him.

J. Michael Straczynski and Shane Davis modernize Superman for the 21st century in SUPERMAN: EARTH ONE in this #1 *New York Times* bestseller.

"A modern, youthful take on the iconic superhero." —*USA Today*

"A Superman for a new generation.... J. Michael Straczynski and Shane Davis managed to breathe a new perspective into the character, full of all the classicism the character demands, but full of all the modernity required to make it fresh for a brand new audience." —*Huffington Post*

"From its poignant domestic moments, delivered in mostly warm, fuzzy flashbacks, to its blockbuster battles, Straczynski's SUPERMAN: EARTH ONE renders like a feature film just waiting for adaptation." —*Wired*

SUPERMAN: EARTH ONE VOL. 1

Writer: J. Michael Straczynski | Artist: Shane Davis | ISBN: 978-1-4012-2469-1 | Diamond Code: FEB130226 | Price: $12.99 | Format: TP

ANIMAL MAN VOL. 1: THE HUNT

Writer: Jeff Lemire | Artist: Travel Foreman

ISBN: 978-1-4012-3507-9 | Diamond Code: FEB120247 | Price: $14.99 | Format: TP

Buddy Baker has gone from "super" man to family man—but is he strong enough to hold his family together when his young daughter starts to manifest her own dangerous powers?

ANIMAL MAN VOL. 2: ANIMAL VS. MAN

Writer: Jeff Lemire | Artist: Steve Pugh

ISBN: 978-1-4012-3800-1 | Diamond Code: OCT120251 | Price: $16.99 | Format: TP

When Buddy goes missing, his family receives assistance from John Constantine and the Justice League Dark.

ANIMAL MAN VOL. 3: ROTWORLD – THE RED KINGDOM

Writer: Jeff Lemire & Scott Snyder | Artist: Steve Pugh

ISBN: 978-1-4012-4262-6 | Diamond Code: JUN130267 | Price: $16.99 | Format: TP

Will Animal Man and Swamp Thing be able to stop the forces of the Rot and change the world back to what it was?

ALL-STAR WESTERN VOL. 1: GUNS AND GOTHAM

Writers: Jimmy Palmiotti & Justin Gray | Artist: Moritat

ISBN: 978-1-4012-3709-7 | Diamond Code: JUL120213 | Price: $16.99 | Format: TP

Jonah Hex teams with Amadeus Arkham to track down a serial killer and search for a missing child in Gotham City during the era of the Wild West.

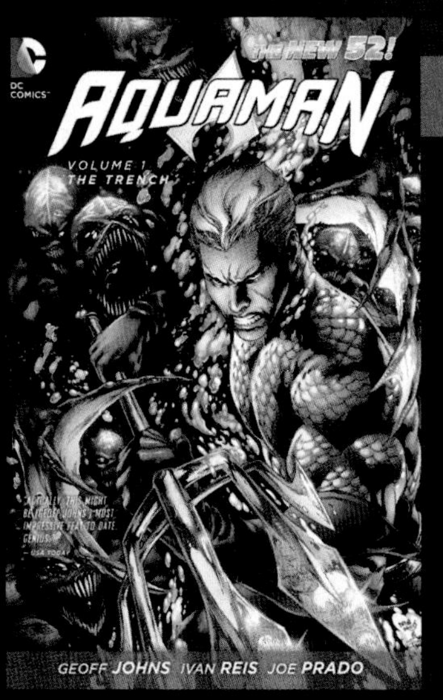

AQUAMAN VOL. 1: THE TRENCH

Writer: Geoff Johns | Artist: Ivan Reis

ISBN: 978-1-4012-3710-3 | Diamond Code: FEB130206

Price $14.99 | Format: TP

Superstar writer Geoff Johns re-teams with artist Ivan Reis to relaunch Aquaman as one of the most powerful and important heroes of the DC Universe.

AQUAMAN VOL. 2: THE OTHERS

Writer: Geoff Johns | Artist: Ivan Reis
ISBN: 978-1-4012-4295-4 | Diamond Code: AUG130295 | Price: $14.99 | Format: TP

Long before the King of the Seven Seas joined the Justice League, Aquaman was a part of another super-team: The Others.

AQUAMAN VOL. 3: THRONE OF ATLANTIS

Writer: Geoff Johns | Artists: Paul Pelletier & Ivan Reis
ISBN: 978-1-4012-4695-2 | Diamond Code: JUL130228 | Price: 16.99 | Format: TP

Atlantis attacks! As the Justice League answers the call, the question remains: which side is Aquaman on?

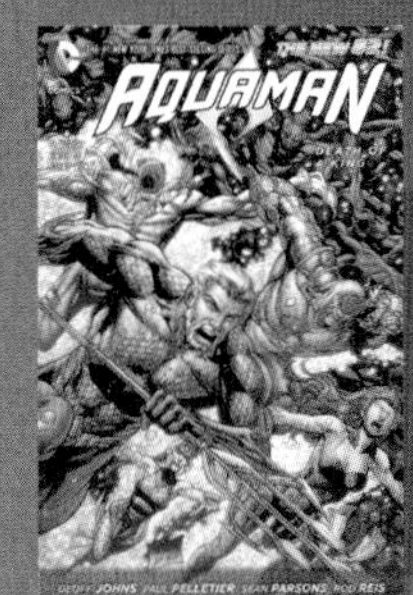

AQUAMAN VOL. 4: DEATH OF A KING

Writer: Geoff Johns | Artist: Paul Pelletier
ISBN: 978-1-4012-4696-9 | Diamond Code: JAN140337 | Price: $24.99 | Format: HC

The dark secrets of Atlantis come back to haunt Aquaman and his allies.

BATGIRL VOL. 1: THE DARKEST REFLECTION

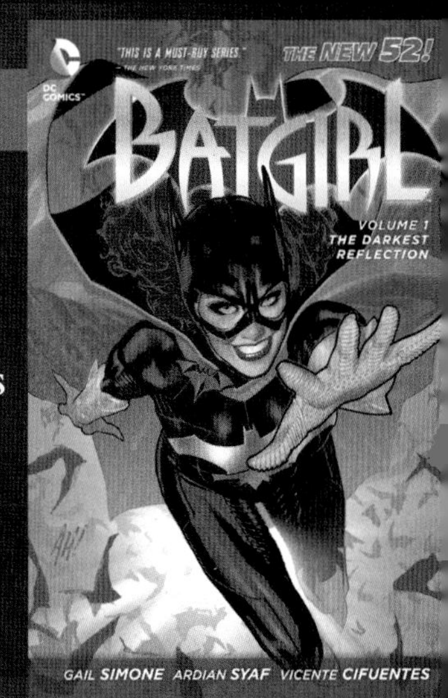

Writer: Gail Simone | Artist: Ardian Syaf
ISBN: 978-1-4012-3814-8 | Diamond Code: NOV120262
Price: $14.99 | Format: TP

Barbara Gordon finally returns as Batgirl in this #1 *New York Times* bestseller.

BATGIRL VOL. 2: KNIGHTFALL DESCENDS

Writer: Gail Simone | Artist: Ed Benes
ISBN: 978-1-4012-3817-9 | Diamond Code: JUL130236 | Price: $16.99 | Format: TP

Batgirl has returned to Gotham, where brand-new foes are waiting to greet her.

BATGIRL VOL. 3: DEATH OF THE FAMILY

Writer: Gail Simone | Artist: Daniel Sampere & Ed Benes

ISBN: 978-1-4012-4628-0 | Diamond Code: FEB140247 | Price: $16.99 | Format: TP

The Joker is back and setting his sights on one of the heroes he's tormented most: Batgirl!

BATGIRL VOL. 4: WANTED

Writers: Gail Simone | Artist: Fernando Pasarin

ISBN: 978-1-4012-4629-7 | Diamond Code: JAN140355 | Price: $24.99 | Format: HC

Batgirl is wanted for murder and her father, Commissioner Gordon, is holding the warrant for her arrest.

BATMAN VOL. 1: THE COURT OF OWLS

Writers: Scott Snyder | Artists: Greg Capullo

ISBN: 978-1-4012-3542-0 | Diamond Code: DEC120323 | Price: $16.99 | Format: TP

A new era for The Dark Knight and Gotham City begins here from writer Scott Snyder and artist Greg Capullo, as Batman and the Bat-Family continue their quest to protect the people of Gotham.

BATMAN VOL. 2: CITY OF OWLS

Writer: Scott Snyder | Artist: Greg Capullo

ISBN: 978-1-4012-3778-3 | Diamond Code: JUL130235 | Price: $16.99 | Format: TP

"Night of the Owls" continues here! Batman must stop the Talons that have breached the Batcave in order to save an innocent life ... and Gotham City!

BATMAN VOL. 3: DEATH OF THE FAMILY

Writer: Scott Snyder | Artist: Greg Capullo

ISBN: 978-1-4012-4234-3 | Diamond Code: MAY130216 | Price: $24.99 | Format: HC

After having his face sliced off one year ago, the Joker makes his horrifying return to Gotham City! How can Batman protect his city and those he's closest to?

BATMAN VOL. 4: ZERO YEAR – SECRET CITY

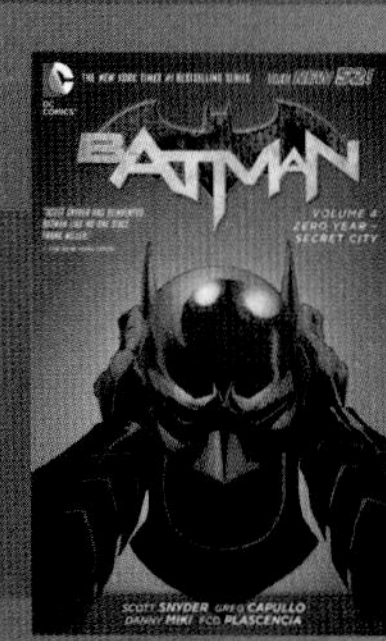

Writer: Scott Snyder | Artist: Greg Capullo

ISBN: 978-1-4012-4508-5 | Diamond Code: JAN140342 | Price: $24.99 | Format: HC

Scott Snyder and Greg Capullo present Batman's origin ... as you've never seen it before!

BATMAN: DETECTIVE COMICS VOL. 1: FACES OF DEATH

Writer: Tony S. Daniel | Artist: Tony S. Daniel

ISBN: 978-1-4012-3467-6 | Diamond Code: FEB120245 | Price: $16.99 | Format: TP

Writer/artist Tony S. Daniel's take on Batman's infamous rogues' gallery.

BATMAN: THE DARK KNIGHT VOL. 1: KNIGHT TERRORS

Writers: David Finch & Paul Jenkins | Artist: David Finch

ISBN: 978-1-4012-3711-0 | Diamond Code: APR130221 | Price: $16.99 | Format: TP

The Dark Knight faces Gotham's supernatural threats.

BATMAN, INCORPORATED VOL. 1: DEMON STAR

Writer: Grant Morrison | Artists: Chris Burnham

ISBN: 978-1-4012-4263-3 | Diamond Code: AUG130293 | Price: $16.99 | Format: TP

Batman and his allies must strengthen their resolve as Leviathan moves to take Gotham City.

BATMAN, INCORPORATED VOL. 2: GOTHAM'S MOST WANTED

Writer: Grant Morrison | Artists: Chris Burnham

ISBN: 978-1-4012-4400-2 | Diamond Code: JUL130233 | Price: $24.99 | Format: HC

Writer Grant Morrison concludes the Batman epic he began nearly a decade ago in BATMAN & SON.

BATMAN/SUPERMAN VOL. 1: CROSS WORLD

Writer: Greg Pak | Artist: Jae Lee

ISBN: 978-1-4012-4509-2 | Diamond Code: DEC130296 | Price: $22.99 | Format: HC

Batman and Superman together in their own team-up series.

BATMAN & ROBIN VOL. 1: BORN TO KILL

Writer: Peter J. Tomasi | Artist: Patrick Gleason

ISBN: 978-1-4012-3838-4 | Diamond Code: MAR120241 | Price: $16.99 | Format: TP

Damian Wayne, Batman's long-lost son, takes over the mantle of the Boy Wonder.

BATMAN & ROBIN VOL. 2: PEARL

Writer: Peter J. Tomasi | Artist: Patrick Gleason
ISBN: 978-1-4012-4267-1 | Diamond Code: FEB130207 | Price: $16.99 | Format: TP

Batman's son Robin must prove to his father—as well as his previous mantle-holders—that he's worthy of being the newest Boy Wonder.

BATMAN & ROBIN VOL. 3: DEATH OF THE FAMILY

Writer: Peter J. Tomasi | Artist: Patrick Gleason
ISBN: 978-1-4012-4268-8 | Diamond Code: JUL130234 | Price: $22.99 | Format: HC

The Joker returns to test Batman and the extended Bat-family!

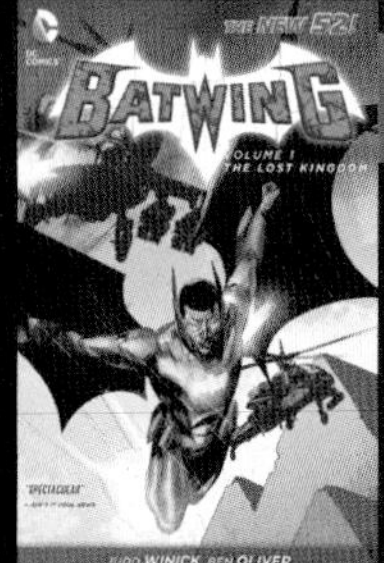

BATWING VOL. 1: THE LOST KINGDOM

Writer: Judd Winick | Artist: Ben Oliver
ISBN: 978-1-4012-3476-8 | Diamond Code: APR120246 | Price: $14.99 | Format: TP

Spinning out of the pages of *Batman, Incorporated,* introducing Africa's greatest hero.

BATWOMAN VOL. 1: HYDROLOGY

Writers: J.H. Williams III & W. Haden Blackman | Artist: J.H. Williams III
ISBN: 978-1-4012-3784-4 | Diamond Code: OCT120253 | Price: $14.99 | Format: TP

J.H. Williams III's beautiful and complex series about Gotham's newest protector in this #1 *New York Times* bestseller.

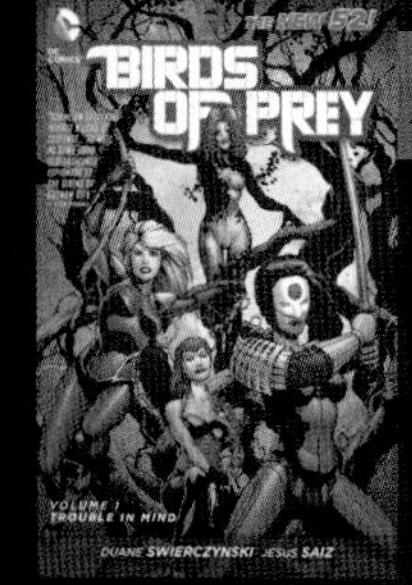

BIRDS OF PREY VOL. 1: TROUBLE IN MIND

Writer: Duane Swierczynski | Artists: Jesús Saíz & Javier Pina
ISBN: 978-1-4012-3699-1 | Diamond Code: JUN120236 | Price: $14.99 | Format: TP

The most dangerous women of the DCU tackle crime on the streets of Gotham.

CATWOMAN VOL. 1: THE GAME

Writer: Judd Winick | Artist: Guillem March
ISBN: 978-1-4012-3464-5| Diamond Code: FEB120248 | Price: $14.99 | Format: TP

Catwoman Selina Kyle is addicted to stealing ... and Batman.

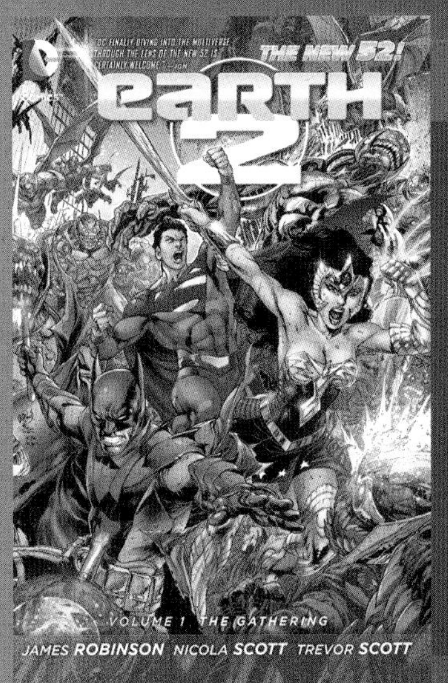

EARTH 2 VOL. 1: THE GATHERING

Writer: James Robinson | Artist: Nicola Scott
ISBN: 978-1-4012-4281-7 | Diamond Code: JUL130241
Price $14.99 | Format: TP

With the Earth—and its greatest heroes—decimated, left in their stead is a group of young, untrained heroes who pick up the pieces in the dusty aftermath.

James Robinson and Nicola Scott bring their own unique twist to classic DC heroes in this graphic novel.

EARTH 2 VOL. 2: TOWER OF FATE

Writer: James Robinson | Artist: Nicola Scott
ISBN: 978-1-4012-4614-3 | Diamond Code: JAN140344 | Price $16.99 | Format: TP

The World Army has begun rounding up the superheroes of Earth 2, but for what reason?

EARTH 2 VOL. 3: WAR

Writer: James Robinson | Artist: Nicola Scott
ISBN: 978-1-4012-4615-0 | Diamond Code: DEC130299 | Price $22.99 | Format: HC

The forces of Apokolips are back to finish the job they started as the heroes of Earth 2 must team with the mysterious new Batman to defeat them.

THE FLASH VOL. 1: MOVE FORWARD

Writers: Francis Manapul & Brian Buccellato | Artist: Francis Manapul
ISBN: 978-1-4012-3554-3 | Diamond Code: MAY130224 | Price: $16.99 | Format: TP

The Fastest Man Alive returns as Central City's greatest protector.

THE FLASH VOL. 2: ROGUES REVOLUTION

Writers: Francis Manapul & Brian Buccellato | Artist: Francis Manapul
ISBN: 978-1-4012-4273-2| Diamond Code: NOV130229 | Price: $16.99 | Format: TP

The Flash's Rogue's Gallery is back, but they are more powerful than ever and they're each looking to take down the Fastest Man Alive!

THE FLASH VOL. 3: GORILLA WARFARE

Writers: Francis Manapul & Brian Buccellato | Artist: Francis Manapul
ISBN: 978-1-4012-4274-9 | Diamond Code: OCT130243 | Price: $24.99 | Format: HC

The Flash will have to turn to his former enemies, the Rogues, if he wants to defeat the invading hordes of Gorilla Grodd.

GREEN ARROW VOL. 1: THE MIDAS TOUCH

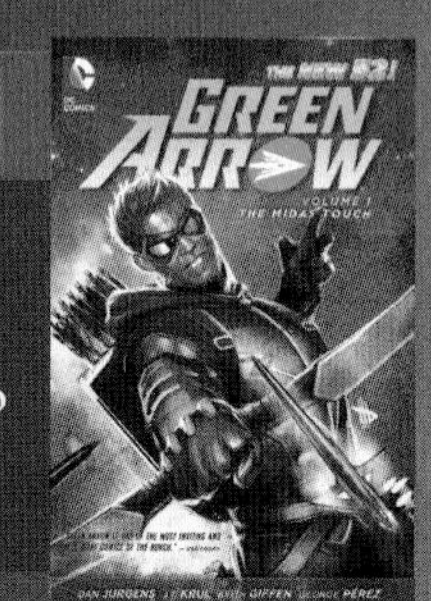

Writers: J.T. Krul & Keith Giffen | Artists: Dan Jurgens & George Pérez
ISBN: 978-1-4012-3486-7 | Diamond Code: FEB120249 | Price: $14.99 | Format: TP

Reimagines the sharp-shooting, emerald-clad DC hero Oliver Queen, also known as Green Arrow!

GREEN ARROW VOL. 4: THE KILL MACHINE

Writer: Jeff Lemire | Artist: Andrea Sorrentino
ISBN: 978-1-4012-4690-7 | Diamond Code: DEC130306 | Price: $16.99 | Format: TP

Jeff Lemire sets Green Arrow off in a bold new direction, starting with startling questions about Oliver's origin—involving his father?

GREEN LANTERN VOL. 1: SINESTRO

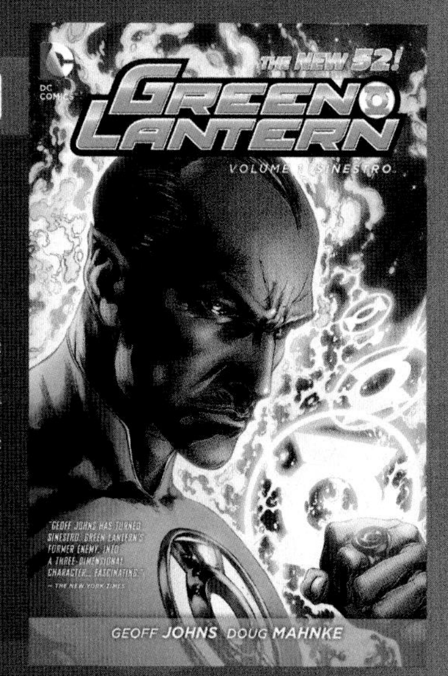

Writer: Geoff Johns | Artist: Doug Mahnke
ISBN: 978-1-4012-3455-3 | Diamond Code: JAN120301
Price: $14.99 | Format: TP

Hal Jordan has been stripped of his ring by the Guardians of the Universe. The unexpected Green Lantern left to defend Sector 2814 in his stead? The Corps' greatest enemy, Sinestro!

GREEN LANTERN VOL. 2: THE REVENGE OF BLACK HAND

Writer: Geoff Johns | Artist: Doug Mahnke
ISBN: 978-1-4012-3767-7 | Diamond Code: JUL130229 | Price: $16.99 | Format: TP

Now teaming up with his former foe, Hal Jordan and Sinestro find themselves investigating a crime that leads them deep into the homeworld of the Indigo Tribe.

GREEN LANTERN VOL. 3: THE END

Writer: Geoff Johns | Artist: Doug Mahnke

ISBN: 978-1-4012-4684-6 | Diamond Code: JAN140338 | Price: $19.99 | Format: TP

Geoff Johns ends his monumental run on Green Lantern.

GREEN LANTERN VOL. 4: DARK DAYS

Writer: Robert Venditti | Artist: Billy Tan

ISBN: 978-1-4012-4744-7 | Diamond Code: DEC130303 | Price: $24.99 | Format: HC

New writer Robert Venditti creates an all-new direction with the new leader of the Green Lantern Corps: Hal Jordan!

GREEN LANTERN: LIGHTS OUT

Writers: Robert Venditti, Van Jensen, Charles Soule & Justin Jordan | Artists: Billy Tan, Bernard Chang, Alessandro Vitti & Brad Walker

ISBN: 978-1-4012-4816-1 | Diamond Code: FEB140249 | Price: $24.99 | Format: HC

The mysterious alien Relic comes to destroy the Green Lantern Corps... for the good of the universe?

GREEN LANTERN CORPS VOL. 1: FEARSOME

Writer: Peter J. Tomasi | Artist: Fernando Pasarin

ISBN: 978-1-4012-3702-8 | Diamond Code: APR130218 | Price: $14.99 | Format: TP

The intergalactic peace-keeping corps faces a threat from the Guardians' past.

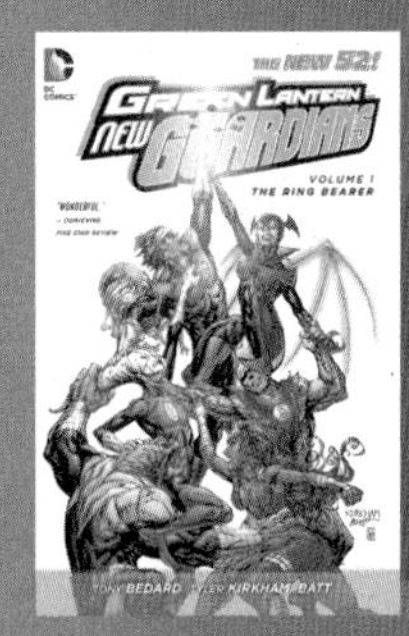

GREEN LANTERN: NEW GUARDIANS VOL. 1: THE RING BEARER

Writer: Tony Bedard | Artist: Tyler Kirkham

ISBN: 978-1-4012-3708-0 | Diamond Code: JUN120235 | Price: $14.99 | Format: TP

Spinning out of *Green Lantern*, members from all the various Lantern Corps tenuously unite into their own team of renegades.

JUSTICE LEAGUE VOL. 1: ORIGIN

Writer: Geoff Johns | Artist: Jim Lee

ISBN: 978-1-4012-3788-2 | Diamond Code: OCT120252 | Price: $16.99 | Format: TP

In one of the most game-changing titles in comic industry history, Geoff Johns and Jim Lee re-imagine the Justice League for the 21st century.

JUSTICE LEAGUE VOL. 2: THE VILLAIN'S JOURNEY

Writer: Geoff Johns | Artist: Jim Lee
ISBN: 978-1-4012-3765-3 | Diamond Code: JUN130261 | Price: $16.99 | Format: TP

A villain from the League's past reemerges and it all ends with one of the most surprising moments in DC history!

JUSTICE LEAGUE VOL. 3: THRONE OF ATLANTIS

Writer: Geoff Johns | Artist: Ivan Reis & Paul Pelletier
ISBN: 978-1-4012-4698-3 | Diamond Code: JAN140339 | Price: $16.99 | Format: TP

The armies of Atlantis attack the surface world pitting the Justice League against one of their own.

JUSTICE LEAGUE VOL. 4: THE GRID

Writer: Geoff Johns | Artist: Ivan Reis
ISBN: 978-1-4012-4717-1 | Diamond Code: DEC130297 | Price: $24.99 | Format: HC

The Justice League becomes embroiled in a battle with the two other Justice Leagues—the Trinity War. But who is the real force behind it all?

JUSTICE LEAGUE: TRINITY WAR

Writers: Geoff Johns & Jeff Lemire | Artists: Ivan Reis, Doug Mahnke & Mikel Janin
ISBN: 978-1-4012-4519-1 | Diamond Code: NOV130226 | Price: $29.99 | Format: HC

The Justice League, Justice League Dark and Justice League of America go to war with one another, with the fate of the universe on the line.

JUSTICE LEAGUE OF AMERICA VOL. 1: WORLD'S MOST DANGEROUS

Writer: Geoff Johns | Artists: David Finch, Brett Booth & Doug Mahnke
ISBN: 978-1-4012-4236-7 | Diamond Code: JUL130230 | Price: $24.99 | Format: HC

The government has signed up their own Justice League, including the unlikeliest of members: Catwoman, Katana, Martian Manhunter, Hawkman, Star Girl and the return of 80s superhero Vibe.

JUSTICE LEAGUE DARK VOL. 1: IN THE DARK

Writer: Peter Milligan | Artist: Mikel Janin
ISBN: 978-1-4012-3704-2 | Diamond Code: JUL120211 | Price: $14.99 | Format: TP

John Constantine leads a ragtag group of heroes against the world's most dangerous supernatural threats.

JUSTICE LEAGUE DARK VOL. 2: THE BOOKS OF MAGIC

Writer: Jeff Lemire | Artist: Mikel Janin

ISBN: 978-1-4012-4024-0 | Diamond Code: APR130217 | Price: $16.99 | Format: TP

Vampires across the world have gone berserk, attacking anything with a pulse.

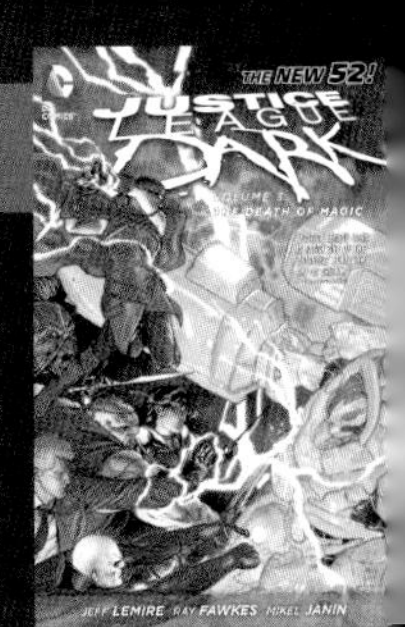

JUSTICE LEAGUE DARK VOL. 3: THE DEATH OF MAGIC

Writers: Jeff Lemire & Ray Fawkes | Artist: Mikel Janin

ISBN: 978-1-4012-4245-9 | Diamond Code: OCT130241 | Price: $16.99 | Format: TP

Transported to another dimension, Tim Hunter and Zatanna awake in a world where magic once ruled in peace until mad scientists banned magic and forced all the magical creatures into exile.

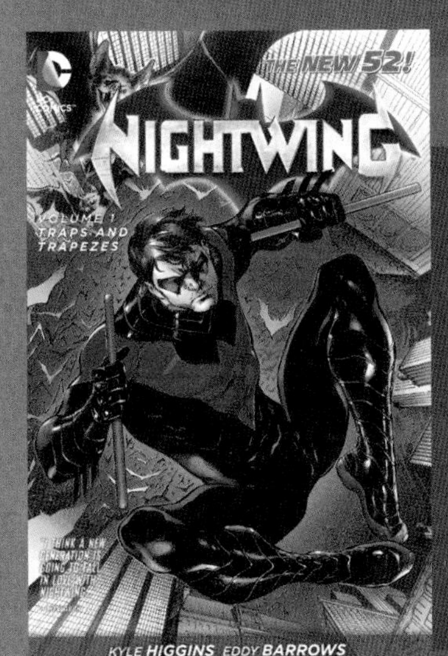

NIGHTWING VOL. 1: TRAPS AND TRAPEZES

Writers: Kyle Higgins | Artist: Eddy Barrows

ISBN: 978-1-4012-3705-9 | Diamond Code: JUL120214

Price: $14.99 | Format: TP

Dick Grayson flies high once more as Nightwing. Returning to the Haly's Circus—his childhood home and the place of his parents' murder—Dick Grayson must confront his past and a greater evil as Nightwing!

NIGHTWING VOL. 2: NIGHT OF THE OWLS

Writer: Kyle Higgins | Artist: Eddy Barrows

ISBN: 978-1-4012-4027-1 | Diamond Code: APR130225 | Price: $14.99 | Format: TP

Dick Grayson must face his past and a deadly adversary in the present as he learns of his connection to the mysterious Court of Owls.

NIGHTWING VOL. 3: DEATH OF THE FAMILY

Writer: Kyle Higgins | Artist: Eddy Barrows

ISBN: 978-1-4012-4413-2 | Diamond Code: SEP130273 | Price: $16.99 | Format: TP

The Joker sets his sights on the members of the Bat-Family and attacks them all where it hurts. For Dick Grayson, that means going after the family he's built up at Haly's Circus!

RED HOOD AND THE OUTLAWS VOL. 1: REDEMPTION

Writer: Scott Lobdell | Artist: Kenneth Rocafort
ISBN: 978-1-4012-3712-7 | Diamond Code: AUG120248 | Price: $14.99 | Format: TP

Former Robin Jason Todd finds himself in an unlikely partnership with fellow misfits Arsenal and the exiled alien princess Starfire.

RED LANTERNS VOL. 1: BLOOD AND RAGE

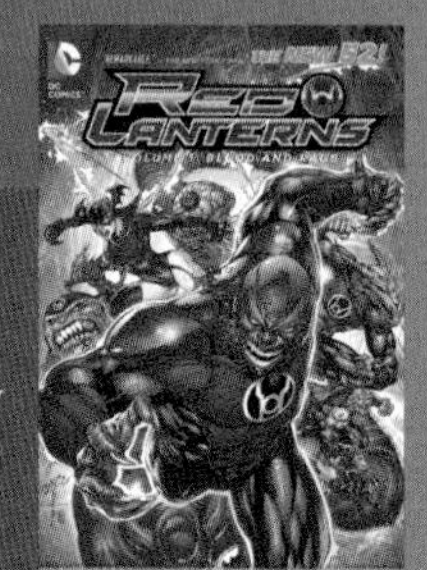

Writer: Peter Milligan | Artist: Ed Benes
ISBN: 978-1-4012-3491-1 | Diamond Code: MAR120243 | Price: $14.99 | Format: TP

Atrocitus, leader of the Red Lanterns, wreaks fiery vengeance on those who prey on the innocent.

STORMWATCH VOL. 1: THE DARK SIDE

Writer: Paul Cornell | Artist: Miguel Sepulveda
ISBN: 978-1-4012-3483-6 | Diamond Code: FEB120251 | Price: $14.99 | Format: TP

The world's most secret organization of superheroes protects the planet from inter-dimensional harm.

SUICIDE SQUAD VOL. 1: KICKED IN THE TEETH

Writer: Adam Glass | Artists: Federico Dallocchio & Clayton Henry
ISBN: 978-1-4012-3544-4 | Diamond Code: APR120250 | Price: $14.99 | Format: TP

A band of former super-villains is recruited by a shadowy government agency for missions so dangerous, it's suicide.

SUPERBOY VOL. 1: INCUBATION

Writer: Scott Lobdell | Artist: R.B. Silva
ISBN: 978-1-4012-3485-0 | Diamond Code: MAY120285 | Price: $14.99 | Format: TP

A secret organization called N.O.W.H.E.R.E. creates their own teenage Kryptonian, but for what nefarious purpose?

SUPERGIRL VOL. 1: LAST DAUGHTER OF KRYPTON

Writers: Michael Green & Mike Johnson | Artist: Mahmud Asrar
ISBN: 978-1-4012-3680-9 | Diamond Code: JUL120216 | Price: $14.99 | Format: TP

Superman's teenaged cousin mysteriously crash-lands on earth decades after the destruction of Krypton.

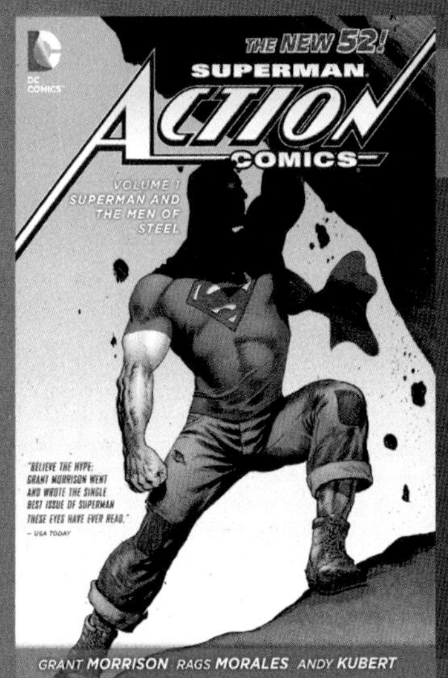

SUPERMAN: ACTION COMICS VOL. 1: SUPERMAN AND THE MEN OF STEEL

Writer: Grant Morrison | Artists: Rags Morales & Andy Kubert
ISBN: 978-1-4012-3547-5 | Diamond Code: FEB130215
Price $16.99 | Format: TP

See humanity's first encounters with Superman, before he became one of the World's Greatest Super Heroes! Set a few years in the past, it's a bold new take on a classic hero.

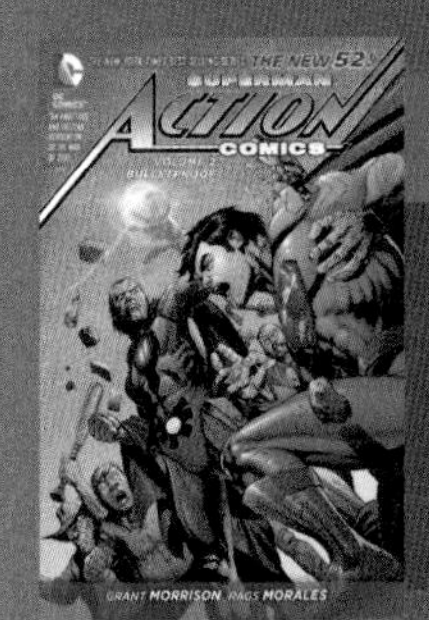

SUPERMAN: ACTION COMICS VOL. 2: BULLETPROOF

Writer: Grant Morrison | Artist: Rags Morales
ISBN: 978-1-4012-4254-1 | Diamond Code: SEP130275 | Price $16.99 | Format: TP

Clark Kent is dead! Grave circumstances cause Superman to leave behind his alter ego.

SUPERMAN: ACTION COMICS VOL. 3: AT THE END OF DAYS

Writer: Grant Morrison | Artist: Rags Morales
ISBN: 978-1-4012-4232-9 | Diamond Code: AUG130298 | Price $24.99 | Format: HC

Grant Morrison finishes his epic run on the Man of Steel, as the multiverse sends its deadliest villains against Superman.

SUPERMAN VOL. 1: WHAT PRICE TOMORROW?

Writer: George Pérez | Artists: Jesús Merino & Nicola Scott
ISBN: 978-1-4012-3686-1 | Diamond Code: MAR130274 | Price: $14.99 | Format: TP

In a world that fears him, Superman must continue to safeguard Metropolis from threats that he himself has created.

SUPERMAN VOL. 2: SECRETS & LIES

Writer: Dan Jurgens | Artists: Keith Giffen & Dan Jurgens
ISBN: 978-1-4012-4257-2 | Diamond Code: FEB130212 | Price: $16.99 | Format: TP

Can Helspont gain control over Superman and use him to execute his invasion plan? Or will the Earth's alien protector cast Helspont back to the planet of Daemon?

SUPERMAN VOL. 3: FURY AT WORLD'S END

Writer: Scott Lobdell | Artist: Kenneth Rocafort
ISBN: 978-1-4012-4320-3 | Diamond Code: SEP130276 | Price: $22.99 | Format: HC

It's all-out war between H'El, Superman, the Justice League, Superboy and Supergirl, but whose side is everyone on?

SWAMP THING VOL. 1: RAISE THEM BONES

Writer: Scott Snyder | Artist: Yanick Paquette
ISBN: 978-1-4012-3462-1 | Diamond Code: MAY120280 | Price: $14.99 | Format: TP

One of the world's most iconic characters returns to the heart of the DC Universe!

SWAMP THING VOL. 2: FAMILY TREE

Writer: Scott Snyder | Artist: Yanick Paquette
ISBN: 978-1-4012-3843-8 | Diamond Code: JAN130301 | Price: $14.99 | Format: TP

Alec Holland is back as the Swamp Thing, fully formed as the protector of The Green!

SWAMP THING VOL. 3: ROTWORLD – THE GREEN KINGDOM

Writers: Scott Snyder & Jeff Lemire | Artist: Yanick Paquette
ISBN: 978-1-4012-4264-0 | Diamond Code: AUG130299 | Price: $16.99 | Format: TP

Swamp Thing finds unlikely allies in Deadman and Poison Ivy, as he ventures into Gotham to find Batman. But will the Caped Crusader be enough to break Rotworld?

TEEN TITANS VOL. 1: IT'S OUR RIGHT TO FIGHT

Writer: Scott Lobdell | Artist: Brett Booth
ISBN: 978-1-4012-3698-4 | Diamond Code: JUN120239 | Price: $14.99 | Format: TP

Scott Lobdell and Brett Booth launch an all-new Teen Titans into new and action-packed adventures!

TEEN TITANS VOL. 2: THE CULLING

Writer: Scott Lobdell | Artist: Brett Booth
ISBN: 978-1-4012-4103-2 | Diamond Code: MAR130272 | Price: $16.99 | Format: TP

The organization known as N.O.W.H.E.R.E. captures Superboy, the Teen Titans, and Legion Lost and pits the young heroes against each other in combat!

TEEN TITANS VOL. 3: DEATH OF THE FAMILY

Writers: Scott Lobdell & Fabian Nicieza | Artist: Brett Booth
ISBN: 978-1-4012-4321-0 | Diamond Code: SEP130274 | Price: $14.99 | Format: TP

The team is finally reunited in the wake of "Death of the Family," but something is very wrong with Red Robin! What did the Joker do?

WONDER WOMAN VOL. 1: BLOOD

Writer: Brian Azzarello | Artists: Cliff Chiang & Tony Akins
ISBN: 978-1-4012-3562-8 | Diamond Code: OCT120256 | Price: $14.99 | Format: TP

Superheroics and ancient myth meet, as critically acclaimed writer Brian Azzarello teams with Cliff Chiang and Tony Akins to begin a new chapter for the Amazon Princess.

WONDER WOMAN VOL. 2: GUTS

Writer: Brian Azzarello | Artists: Cliff Chiang & Tony Akins
ISBN: 978-1-4012-3810-0 | Diamond Code: JUN130271 | Price: $14.99 | Format: TP

Wonder Woman goes to hell! After playing Poseidon, Hades, and Hera against each other, Hades strikes back by kidnapping Zola and trapping her in the Underworld.

WONDER WOMAN VOL. 3: IRON

Writer: Brian Azzarello | Artists: Cliff Chiang & Tony Akins
ISBN: 978-1-4012-4607-5 | Diamond Code: MAY130226 | Price: $16.99 | Format: TP

As Wonder Woman digs deeper into her familial tree, she finds there are as many Gods that are willing to lend her a hand as there are those that would do her harm.

WONDER WOMAN VOL. 4: WAR

Writer: Brian Azzarello | Artists: Cliff Chiang & Tony Akins
ISBN: 978-1-4012-4608-2 | Diamond Code: NOV130234 | Price: $22.99 | Format: HC

Meet the new God of War: Wonder Woman!

WORLDS' FINEST VOL. 1: THE LOST DAUGHTERS OF EARTH 2

Writer: Paul Levitz | Artists: George Peréz & Kevin Maguire
ISBN: 978-1-4012-3834-6 | Diamond Code: JAN130302 | Price: $14.99 | Format: TP

Stranded on a world not their own, Power Girl and Huntress—the former Supergirl and Robin of Earth 2—must find a way back home.

75
75 YEARS OF BATMAN

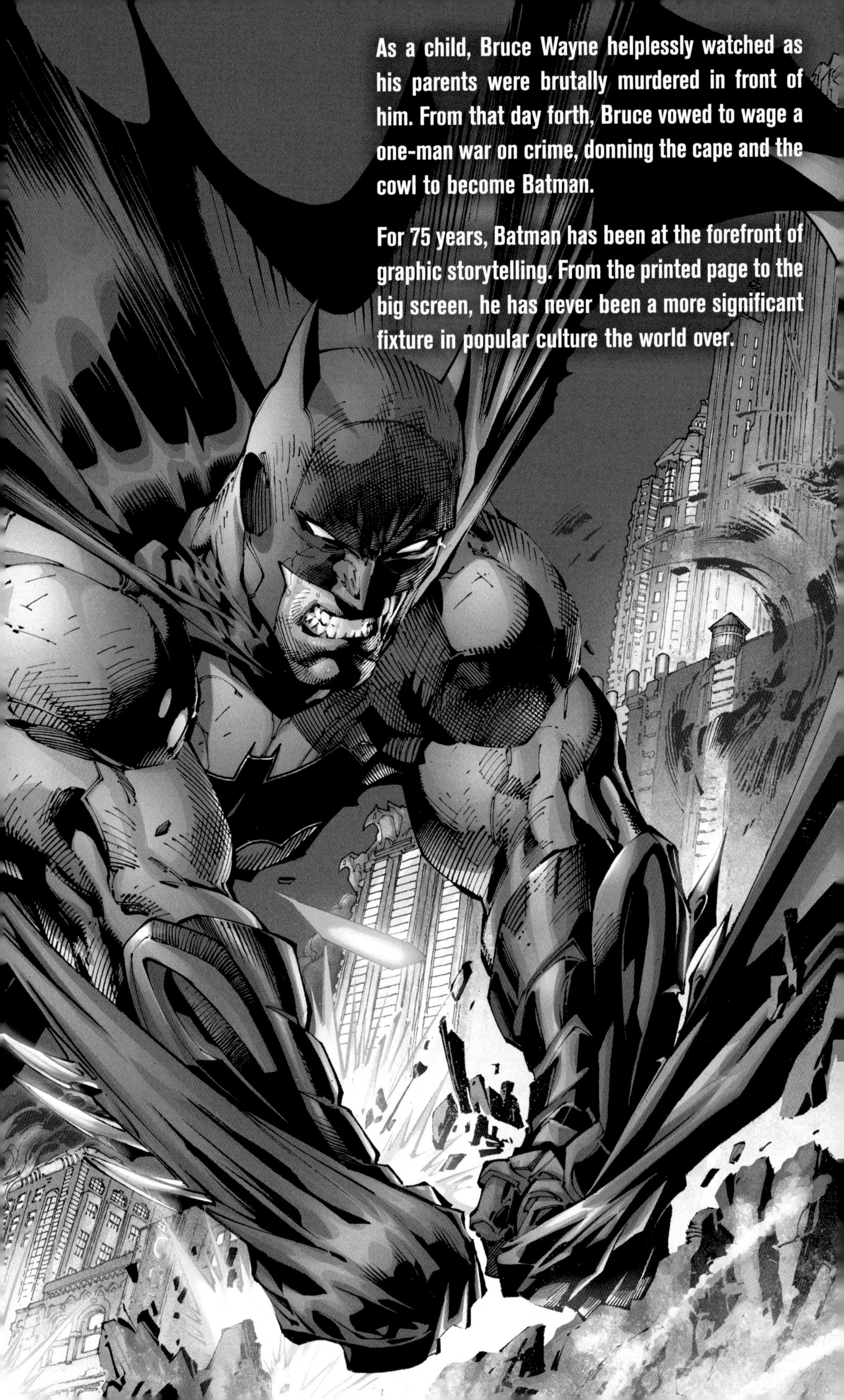

As a child, Bruce Wayne helplessly watched as his parents were brutally murdered in front of him. From that day forth, Bruce vowed to wage a one-man war on crime, donning the cape and the cowl to become Batman.

For 75 years, Batman has been at the forefront of graphic storytelling. From the printed page to the big screen, he has never been a more significant fixture in popular culture the world over.

BATMAN: YEAR ONE

Writer: Frank Miller | Artist: David Mazzucchelli
ISBN: 978-1-4012-0752-6 | Diamond Code: OCT060163 | Price: $14.99 | Format: TP

Frank Miller's genre-defining graphic novel detailing a rookie Dark Knight's first year in Gotham City.

BATMAN: THE LONG HALLOWEEN

Writer: Jeph Loeb | Artist: Tim Sale
ISBN: 978-1-4012-3259-7 | Diamond Code: JUL110251 | Price: $24.99 | Format: TP

A Batman murder mystery written by Jeph Loeb with art by Tim Sale, set during the Dark Knight's early days as he must race against the calendar to discover the identity of the serial killer Holiday.

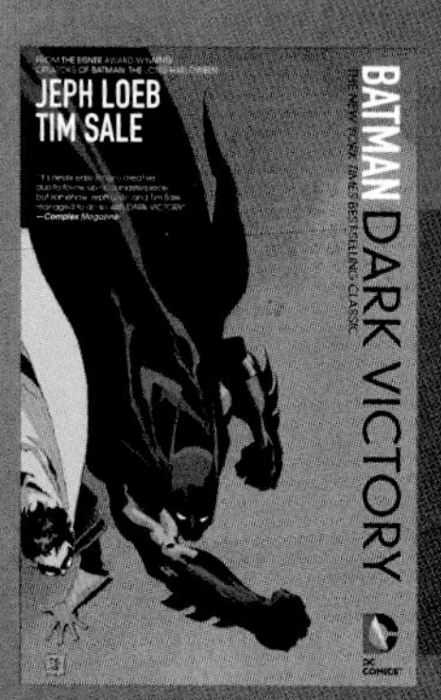

BATMAN: DARK VICTORY

Writer: Jeph Loeb | Artist: Tim Sale
ISBN: 978-1-4012-4401-9 | Diamond Code: NOV130237 | Price: $24.99 | Format: TP

In this sequel to *Batman: The Long Halloween*, Batman faces another seemingly unsolvable mystery, as the Hangman runs through a murder spree in Gotham City.

BATMAN: ARKHAM ASYLUM

Writer: Grant Morrison | Artist: Dave McKean
ISBN: 978-1-4012-0425-9 | Diamond Code: AUG050185 | Price: $17.99 | Format: TP

Grant Morrison and Dave McKean's psychological horror story from Arkham Asylum, home to Gotham City's most deranged super-criminals.

FOR MATURE READERS

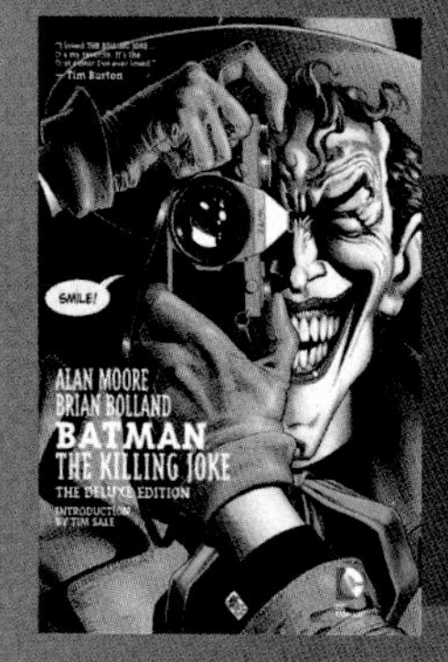

BATMAN: THE KILLING JOKE

Writer: Alan Moore | Artist: Brian Bolland
ISBN: 978-1-4012-1667-2 | Diamond Code: NOV070226 | Price: $17.99 | Format: HC

The Joker, Batman's greatest adversary, in his definitive origin story by Alan Moore with breathtaking art by Brian Bolland.

FOR MATURE READERS

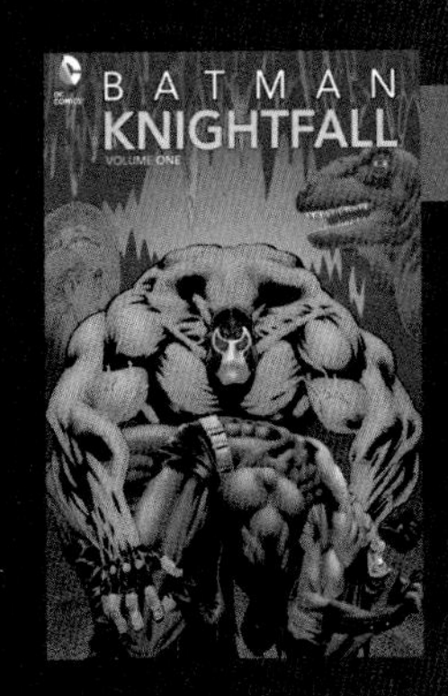

BATMAN: KNIGHTFALL VOL. 1

Writer: Various | Artist: Various
ISBN: 978-1-4012-3379-2 | Diamond Code: JAN120303 | Price: $29.99 | Format: TP

Batman's entire rogues' gallery is freed from Arkham Asylum by the villainous Bane, who tests the Dark Knight mentally and physically as never before.

BATMAN: HUSH

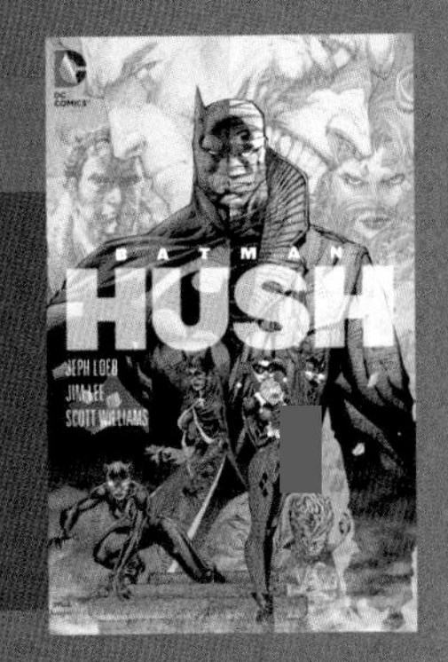

Writer: Jeph Loeb | Artist: Jim Lee
ISBN: 978-1-4012-2317-5 | Diamond Code: MAY090178 | Price: $24.99 | Format: TP

The all-star team of Jeph Loeb and Jim Lee trace the tale of Batman as he seeks to stop a new and deadly villain who seems to know more about Batman than anyone—Hush!

BATMAN: UNDER THE RED HOOD

Writer: Judd Winick | Artist: Doug Mahnke
ISBN: 978-1-4012-3145-3 | Diamond Code: MAY110241 | Price: $29.99 | Format: TP

The Red Hood returns to Gotham City and his shocking actions—as well as his identity—will change Batman forever.

BATMAN AND SON

Writer: Grant Morrison | Artists: Andy Kubert, J.H. Williams III & Tony S. Daniel
ISBN: 978-1-4012-4402-6 | Diamond Code: OCT130238 | Price: $19.99 | Format: TP

In Grant Morrison's epic Batman run, Bruce discovers that he's sired a son, Damian Wayne. Also included is *Batman: The Black Glove* by Morrison with art by J.H. Williams III.

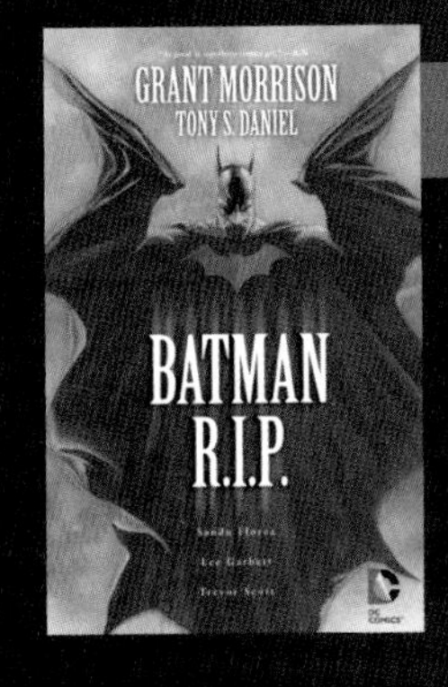

BATMAN: R.I.P.

Writer: Grant Morrison | Artist: Tony S. Daniel
ISBN: 978-1-4012-2576-6 | Diamond Code: MAR100237 | Price: $14.99 | Format: TP

Grant Morrison continues his grand Batman storyline, pitting the Dark Knight against the Black Glove in a prelude to *Final Crisis.*

BATMAN & ROBIN VOL. 1: BATMAN REBORN

Writer: Grant Morrison | Artists: Frank Quitely & Philip Tan

ISBN: 978-1-4012-2987-0 | Diamond Code: DEC100246 | Price: $14.99 | Format: TP

The dynamic duo is reborn, with Dick Grayson donning the cowl along with new Robin Damian Wayne.

BATMAN INCORPORATED

Writer: Grant Morrison | Artist: Yanick Paquette

ISBN: 978-1-4012-3827-8 | Diamond Code: OCT120258 | Price: $19.99 | Format: TP

Batman deputizes different "Batmen" in nations around the globe, creating the indomitable Batman, Incorporated.

BATMAN: THE BLACK MIRROR

Writer: Scott Snyder | Artists: Jock & Francesco Francavilla

ISBN: 978-1-4012-3207-8 | Diamond Code: NOV120268 | Price: $16.99 | Format: TP

The past comes back to haunt Commissioner Gordon and Batman by way of a diabolical murder mystery, in this dark graphic novel that launched writer Scott Snyder into superstardom.

BATMAN VOL. 1: THE COURT OF OWLS

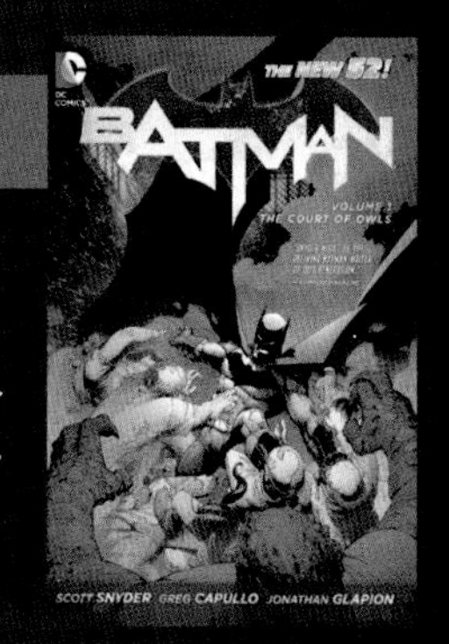

Writer: Scott Snyder | Artist: Greg Capullo

ISBN: 978-1-4012-3542-0 | Diamond Code: JUL130235 | Price: $16.99 | Format: TP

A new era for The Dark Knight and Gotham City begins here from writer Scott Snyder and artist Greg Capullo, as Batman and the Bat-Family continue their quest to protect the people of Gotham.

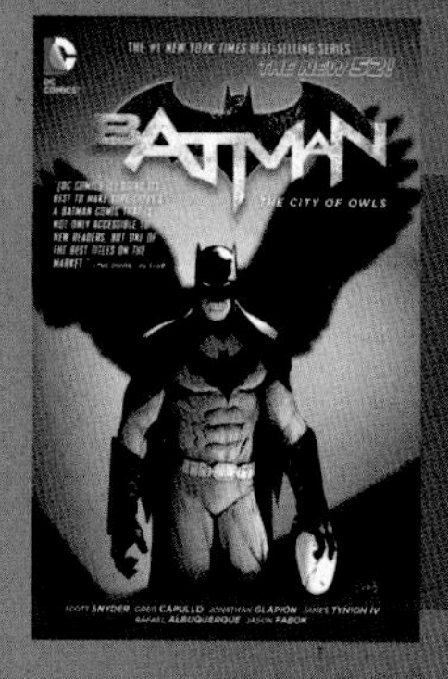

BATMAN VOL. 2: CITY OF OWLS

Writer: Scott Snyder | Artist: Greg Capullo

ISBN: 978-1-4012-3778-3 | Diamond Code: DEC120323 | Price: $16.99 | Format: TP

"Night of the Owls" continues here! Batman must stop the TALONS that have breached the Batcave in order to save an innocent life ... and Gotham City!

BATMAN VOL. 3: DEATH OF THE FAMILY

Writer: Scott Snyder | Artist: Greg Capullo

ISBN: 978-1-4012-4234-3 | Diamond Code: MAY130216 | Price: $24.99 | Format: HC

After having his face sliced off one year ago, the Joker makes his horrifying return to Gotham City! How can Batman protect his city and those he's closest to?

BATMAN VOL. 4: ZERO YEAR – SECRET CITY

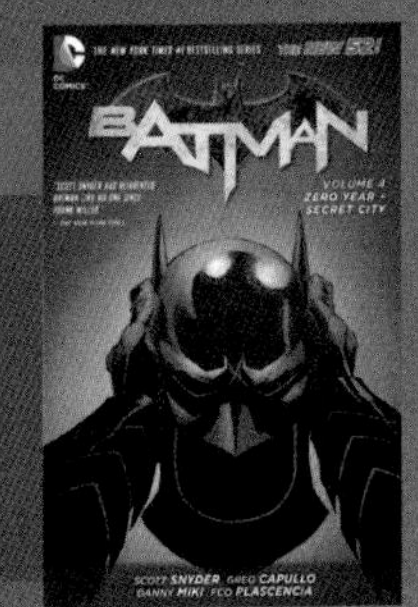

Writer: Scott Snyder | Artist: Greg Capullo

ISBN: 978-1-4012-4508-5 | Diamond Code: JAN140342 | Price: $24.99 | Format: HC

Scott Snyder and Greg Capullo present Batman's origin…as you've never seen it before!

BATMAN & ROBIN VOL. 1: BORN TO KILL

Writer: Peter J. Tomasi | Artist: Patrick Gleason

ISBN: 978-1-4012-3838-4 | Diamond Code: MAR130270 | Price: $16.99 | Format: TP

The Dynamic Duo toil as father and son in this series by the creative team behind the *Green Lantern Corps*—Peter Tomasi and Patrick Gleason.

BATMAN: EARTH ONE

Writer: Geoff Johns | Artist: Gary Frank

ISBN: 978-1-4012-3208-5 | Diamond Code: MAR120234 | Price: $22.99 | Format: HC

Geoff Johns re-imagines the Dark Knight's origin story in this #1 *New York Times* bestseller.

BATMAN: THE DARK KNIGHT RETURNS

Writer: Frank Miller | Artist: Frank Miller

ISBN: 978-1-5638-9342-1 | Diamond Code: NOV118095 | Price: $19.99 | Format: TP

Frank Miller's classic and gritty take on the return of Gotham's hero.

BATMAN: THE DARK KNIGHT STRIKES AGAIN

Writer: Frank Miller | Artist: Frank Miller

ISBN: 978-1-5638-9929-4 | Diamond Code: FEB058404 | Price: $19.99 | Format: TP

The sequel to *Batman: The Dark Knight Returns*, in which Batman must come back once more to save a rapidly decaying world.

SUPERMAN

Rocketed to Earth from the dying planet Krypton, baby Kal-El was raised on Earth by a kindly farming couple. Clark Kent, as he was renamed, grew up and discovered that he had extraordinary powers far exceeding everyone around him. Combined with the strong moral values his adoptive parents instilled in him, he became Superman. Created by Jerry Siegel and Joe Shuster, the Man of Steel was the first—and now most recognized—superhero in pop culture.

SUPERMAN CHRONICLES VOL. 1

Writer: Jerry Siegel | Artist: Joe Shuster
ISBN: 978-1-4012-0764-9 | Diamond Code: NOV050250 | Price: $17.99 | Format: TP

The first adventures of the Man of Steel.

SUPERMAN: A CELEBRATION OF 75 YEARS

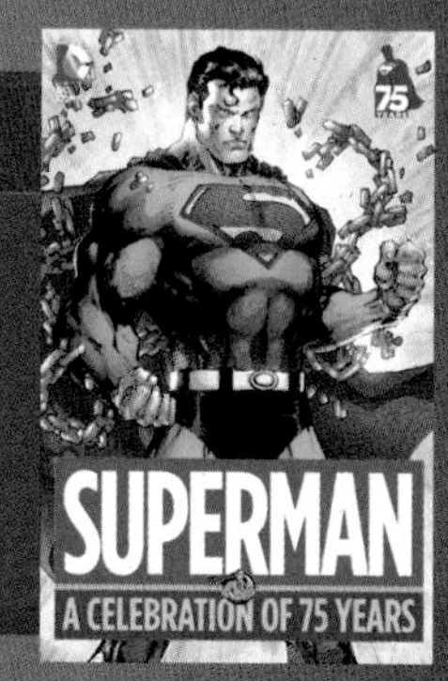

Writers: Various | Artists: Various
ISBN: 978-1-4012-4704-1 | Diamond Code: JUL130224 | Price: $39.99 | Format: HC

This collection gathers a range of stories featuring the first and greatest superhero, highlighting the many roles the Man of Steel has played over the decades.

SUPERMAN: WHATEVER HAPPENED TO THE MAN OF TOMORROW?

Writer: Alan Moore | Artists: Curt Swan & George Pérez
ISBN: 978-1-4012-2731-9 | Diamond Code: APR100219 | Price: $14.99 | Format: TP

Alan Moore's quintessential Superman story.

SUPERMAN: MAN OF STEEL VOL. 1

Writer: John Byrne | Artist: John Byrne
ISBN: 978-0-9302-8928-7 | Diamond Code: JUL058226 | Price: $14.99 | Format: TP

The first re-telling of Superman's epic origin!

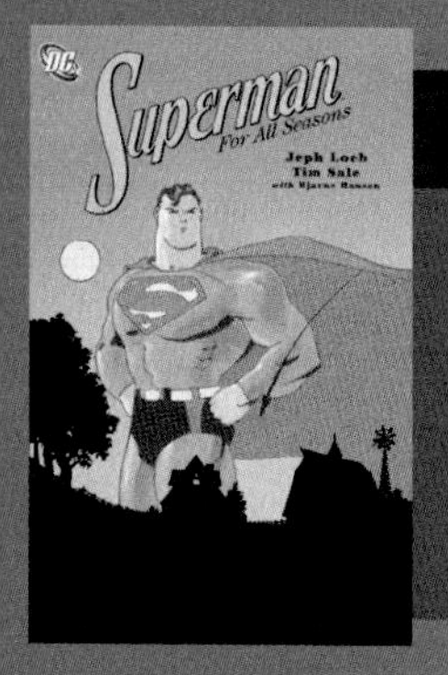

SUPERMAN: FOR ALL SEASONS

Writer: Jeph Loeb | Artist: Tim Sale
ISBN: 978-1-5638-9529-6 | Diamond Code: FEB068194 | Price: $17.99 | Format: TP

The tale of Clark Kent's transformation from country boy to Metropolis Superman as told by the acclaimed duo of Jeph Loeb and Tim Sale.

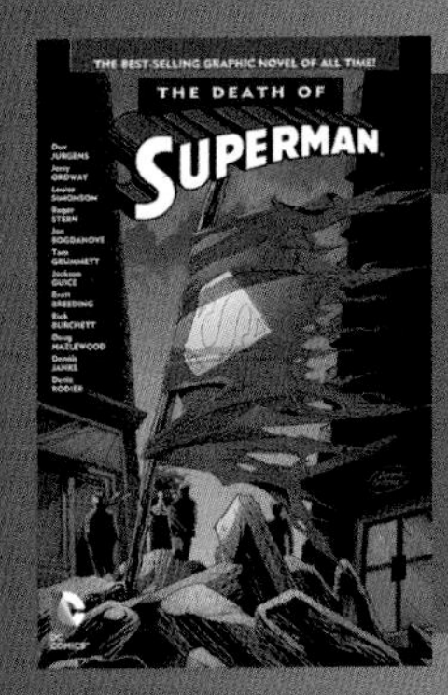

SUPERMAN: THE DEATH OF SUPERMAN

Writer: Various | Artist: Various
ISBN: 978-1-4012-4182-7 | Diamond Code: OCT120269 | Price: $14.99 | Format: TP

The story that shocked the world! Superman pays the ultimate price to stop the killing machine Doomsday.

SUPERMAN/BATMAN VOL. 1

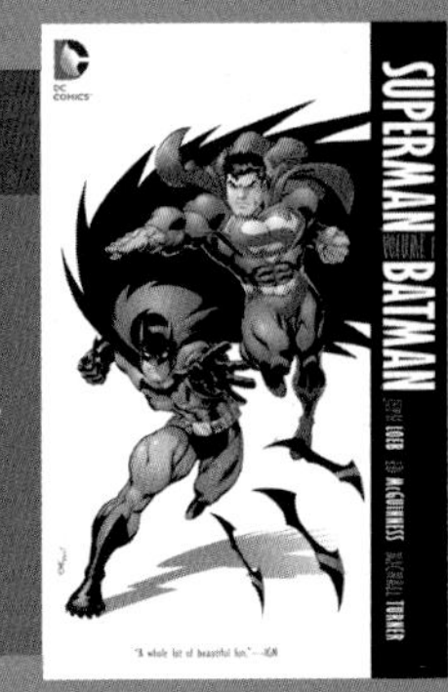

Writer: Jeph Loeb | Artists: Ed McGuinness & Michael Turner
ISBN: 978-1-4012-4818-5 | Diamond Code: JAN140354 | Price: $19.99 | Format: TP

Superman and Batman team-up to combat the machinations of President of the United States Lex Luthor and Darkseid, as the new Supergirl emerges!

LUTHOR

Writer: Brian Azzarello | Artist: Lee Bermejo
ISBN: 978-1-4012-2930-6 | Diamond Code: JUN100212 | Price: $19.99 | Format: HC

The all-star team of Brian Azzarello and Lee Bermejo explores the mind of the Superman's greatest villain Lex Luthor.

SUPERMAN: FOR TOMORROW

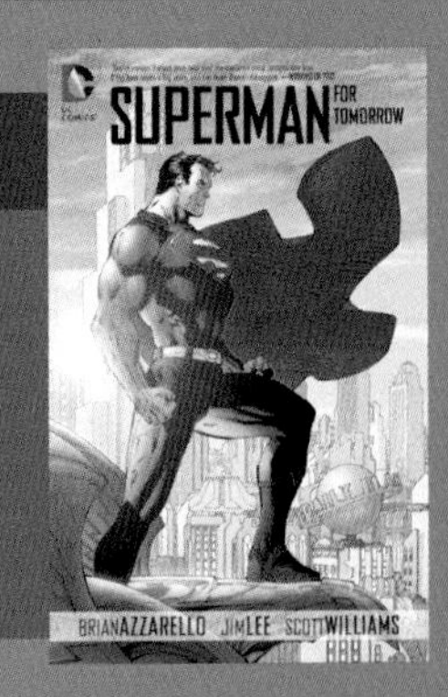

Writer: Brian Azzarello | Artist: Jim Lee
ISBN: 978-1-4012-3780-6 | Diamond Code: NOV120270 | Price: $24.99 | Format: TP

A cataclysmic event has caused half of the Earth's population to disappear and no one is left unaffected, including Superman in this graphic novel by the superstar team of Jim Lee and Brian Azzarello.

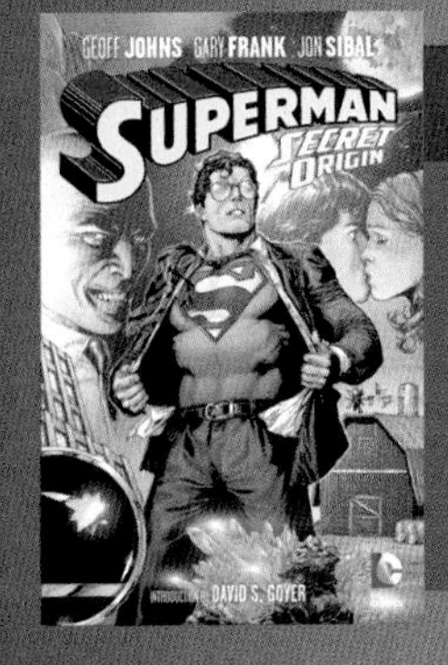

SUPERMAN: SECRET ORIGIN

Writer: Geoff Johns | Artist: Gary Frank
ISBN: 978-1-4012-3299-3 | Diamond Code: SEP110188 | Price: $19.99 | Format: TP

The origin of Superman as told by the *New York Times* best-selling team of Geoff Johns and Gary Frank.

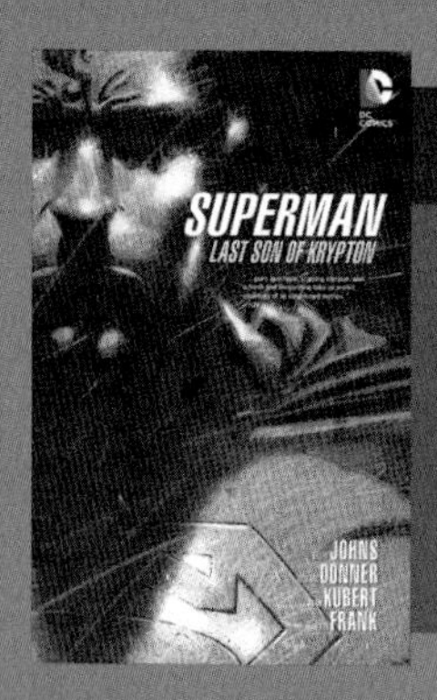

SUPERMAN: LAST SON OF KRYPTON

Writers: Geoff Johns & Richard Donner | Artists: Adam Kubert & Gary Frank
ISBN: 978-1-4012-3779-0 | Diamond Code: OCT120270 | Price: $19.99 | Format: TP

Film director Richard Donner and Geoff Johns pit the Man of Steel against General Zod and Brainiac in these stories illustrated by Adam Kubert and Gary Frank.

SUPERMAN: ESCAPE FROM BIZARRO WORLD

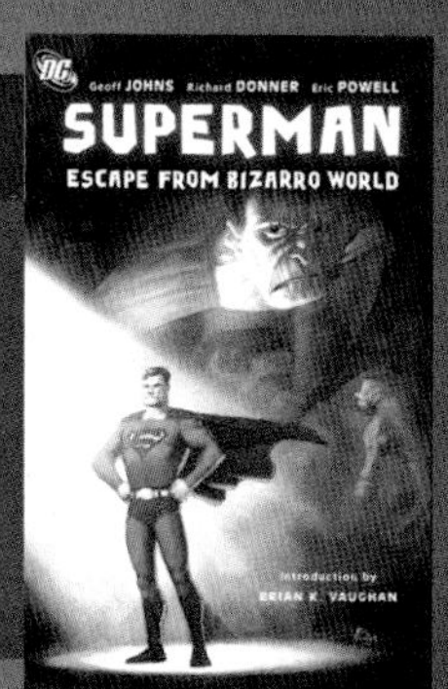

Writers: Geoff Johns & Richard Donner | Artist: Eric Powell
ISBN: 978-1-4012-2033-4 | Diamond Code: FEB090217 | Price: $14.99 | Format: TP

The sequel to SUPERMAN: LAST SON, in which Superman travels to the backwards planet Bizarro World.

SUPERMAN AND THE LEGION OF SUPERHEROES

Writer: Geoff Johns | Artist: Gary Frank
ISBN: 978-1-4012-1904-8 | Diamond Code: APR090217 | Price: $14.99 | Format: TP

The first meeting between Superman and the Legion of Superheroes.

SUPERMAN: ACTION COMICS VOL. 1: SUPERMAN AND THE MEN OF STEEL

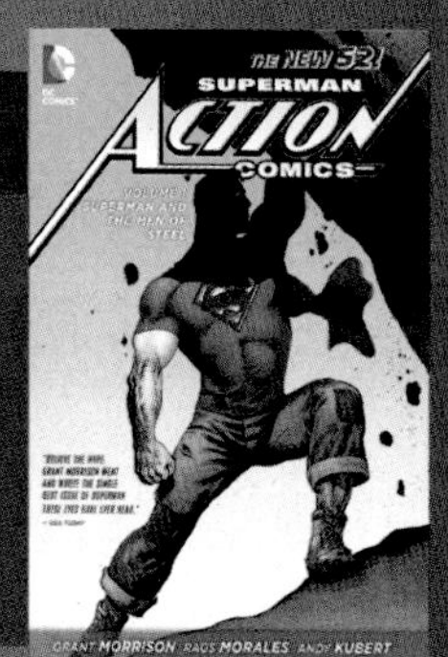

Writer: Grant Morrison | Artists: Rags Morales & Andy Kubert
ISBN: 978-1-4012-3547-5 | Diamond Code: FEB130215 | Price: $16.99 | Format: TP

Grant Morrison returns to the Man of Steel, joined by sensational artist Rags Morales to bring you the story of the early days of Superman.

SUPERMAN VOL. 1: WHAT PRICE TOMORROW?

Writer: George Pérez | Artists: Jesús Merino & Nicola Scott
ISBN: 978-1-4012-3686-1 | Diamond Code: MAR130274 | Price: $14.99 | Format: TP

The Man of Steel flies into the new DC Universe with a new status quo but a continued quest for truth and justice!

SUPERMAN: EARTH ONE VOL. 1

Writer: J. Michael Straczynski | Artist: Shane Davis
ISBN: 978-1-4012-2469-1 | Diamond Code: FEB130226 | Price: $12.99 | Format: TP

The #1 *New York Times* best-selling original graphic novel that re-imagines Superman as a brooding, reluctant hero in modern-day Metropolis.

SUPERMAN: EARTH ONE VOL. 2

Writer: J. Michael Straczynski | Artist: Shane Davis
ISBN: 978-1-4012-3559-8 | Diamond Code: DEC130312 | Price: $14.99 | Format: TP

The sequel to the #1 *New York Times* best-selling original graphic novel by J. Michael Straczynski and Shane Davis.

SUPERMAN: BIRTHRIGHT

Writer: Mark Waid | Artist: Leinil Francis Yu
ISBN: 978-1-4012-0252-1 | Diamond Code: JUL050214 | Price: $19.99 | Format: TP

Superstar writer Mark Waid updates the origin of the Man of Steel in this classic tale.

ALL-STAR SUPERMAN

Writer: Grant Morrison | Artist: Frank Quitely
ISBN: 978-1-4012-3205-4 | Diamond Code: JUL110247 | Price: $29.99 | Format: TP

The critically acclaimed series that harkens back to the Golden Age of Superman by superstar writer Grant Morrison and artist Frank Quitely.

SUPERMAN: RED SON

Writer: Mark Millar | Artists: Dave Johnson & Kilian Plunkett
ISBN: 978-1-4012-0191-3 | Diamond Code: NOV058130 | Price: $17.99 | Format: TP

What if Superman's rocket crash landed in Russia? The Man of Steel is reimagined here as a Soviet hero.

When a dying alien crashes on Earth, reckless test pilot Hal Jordan is chosen to be that alien's successor in the Green Lantern Corps, a universe-wide peacekeeping force. The newest Green Lantern now faces his greatest fears and the most dangerous villains in the universe, armed with a power ring that has the ability to create anything he can imagine. Hal Jordan has become one of the most iconic and popular superheroes of the DC Universe.

GREEN LANTERN: REBIRTH

Writer: Geoff Johns | Artist: Ethan Van Sciver
ISBN: 978-1-4012-2755-5 | Diamond Code: FEB100185 | Price: $14.99 | Format: TP

A jaw-dropping epic that reintroduces the quintessential Green Lantern, Hal Jordan!

GREEN LANTERN: NO FEAR

Writer: Geoff Johns | Artists: Carlos Pacheco & Ethan Van Sciver
ISBN: 978-1-4012-1058-8 | Diamond Code: FEB080244 | Price: $12.99 | Format: TP

Hal Jordan is back from the dead and tries to re-establish his life, though Manhunters and other villains stand in his way.

GREEN LANTERN: REVENGE OF THE GREEN LANTERNS

Writer: Geoff Johns | Artists: Carlos Pacheco, Ethan Van Sciver & Ivan Reis
ISBN: 978-1-4012-0960-5 | Diamond Code: OCT080170 | Price: $14.99 | Format: TP

Hal Jordan discovers that several long-lost Green Lanterns are still alive ... and it's up to him to set them free.

GREEN LANTERN: WANTED: HAL JORDAN

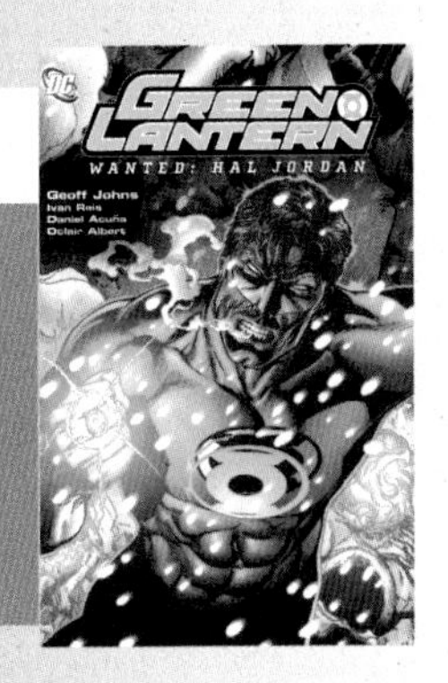

Writer: Geoff Johns | Artists: Ivan Reis & Daniel Acuna
ISBN: 978-1-4012-1590-3 | Diamond Code: OCT080170 | Price: $14.99 | Format: TP

Hunted by the Global Guardians for a crime he didn't commit, can Hal clear his name before it's too late?

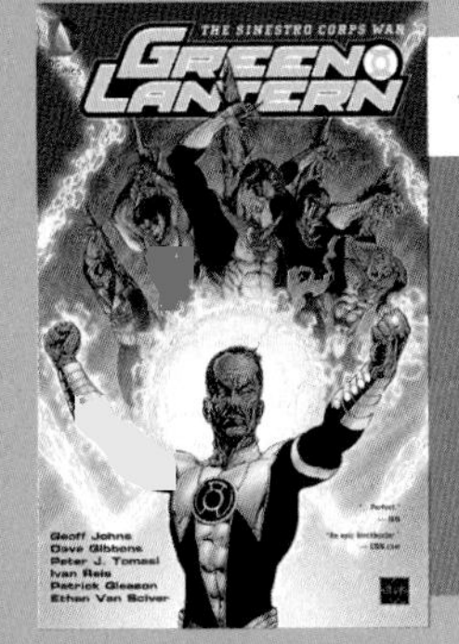

GREEN LANTERN: THE SINESTRO CORPS WAR

Writers: Geoff Johns, Dave Gibbons & Peter J. Tomasi
Artists: Ethan Van Sciver, Ivan Reis & Patrick Gleason
ISBN: 978-1-4012-3301-3 | Diamond Code: JUN110275 | Price: $29.99 | Format: TP

Sinestro—Hal Jordan's former mentor and archnemesis—has gathered an army of soldiers fueled by the fear to do war with the Green Lantern Corps.

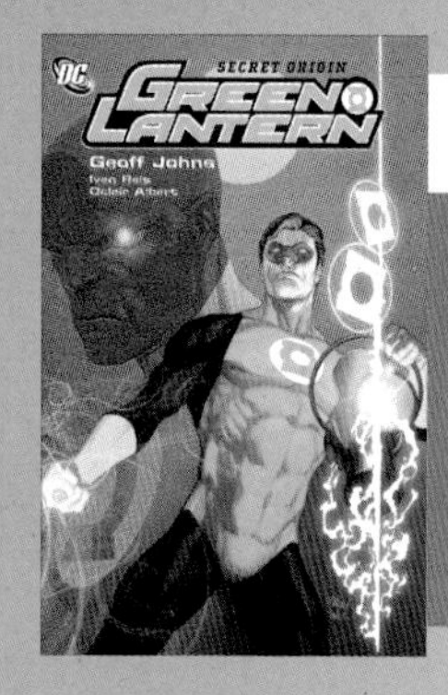

GREEN LANTERN: SECRET ORIGIN

Writer: Geoff Johns | Artist: Ivan Reis
ISBN: 978-1-4012-2017-4 | Diamond Code: AUG108201 | Price: $14.99 | Format: TP

Witness the beginnings of the greatest Green Lantern of all in this title.

GREEN LANTERN: RAGE OF THE RED LANTERNS

Writer: Geoff Johns | Artists: Ivan Reis, Mike McKone & Shane Davis
ISBN: 978-1-4012-2302-1 | Diamond Code: APR100214 | Price: $14.99 | Format: TP

Hal Jordan battles for his life when the Red Lantern Corps, a brutal brigade of monsters fueled by rage, attacks!

GREEN LANTERN: AGENT ORANGE

Writer: Geoff Johns | Artist: Philip Tan
ISBN: 978-1-4012-2420-2 | Diamond Code: AUG100204 | Price: $14.99 | Format: TP

Hal Jordan must battle the bizarre Orange Lantern Corps and its leader, Agent Orange, as they threaten to consume the universe.

BLACKEST NIGHT

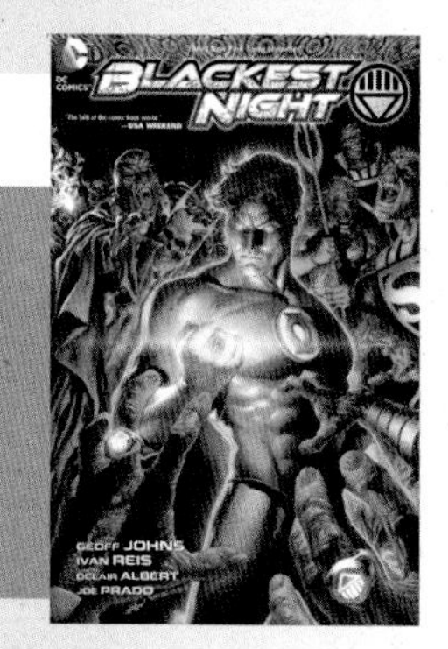

Writer: Geoff Johns | Artist: Ivan Reis
ISBN: 978-1-4012-2953-5 | Diamond Code: APR110192 | Price: $19.99 | Format: TP

Hal Jordan and the Green Lantern Corps lead DC's champions into battle to save the universe from an army of undead Black Lanterns!

BLACKEST NIGHT: GREEN LANTERN

Writer: Geoff Johns | Artist: Doug Mahnke
ISBN: 978-1-4012-2952-8 | Diamond Code: APR110193 | Price: $19.99 | Format: TP

The must-read companion graphic novel to the epic *Blackest Night*.

GREEN LANTERN: BRIGHTEST DAY

Writer: Geoff Johns | Artist: Doug Mahnke
ISBN: 978-1-4012-3141-5 | Diamond Code: FEB120254 | Price: $19.99 | Format: TP

The multi-colored Lantern Corps reluctantly team together to discover what (or who) is behind the mysterious White Lantern.

GREEN LANTERN: WAR OF THE GREEN LANTERNS

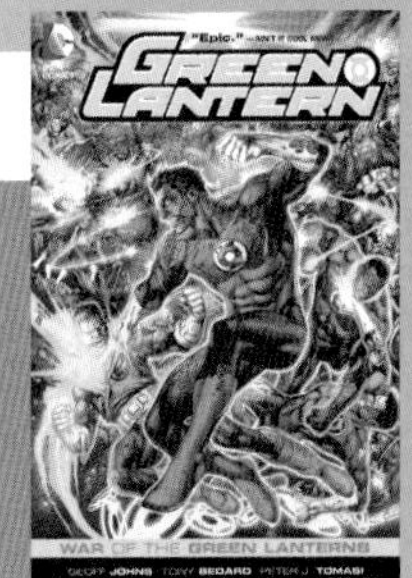

Writers: Geoff Johns, Tony Bedard & Peter J. Tomasi
Artists: Doug Mahnke, Tyler Kirkham & Fernando Pasarin
ISBN: 978-1-4012-3452-2 | Diamond Code: JUN120246 | Price: $16.99 | Format: TP

An ancient evil returns to destroy the Green Lanterns from within, as Corpsmen turn on each other!

GREEN LANTERN VOL. 1: SINESTRO

Writer: Geoff Johns | Artist: Doug Mahnke
ISBN: 978-1-4012-3455-3 | Diamond Code: JAN120301 | Price: $14.99 | Format: TP

Hal Jordan has been stripped of his ring. Left is an unexpected new Green Lantern in town: Sinestro!

GREEN LANTERN VOL. 2: THE REVENGE OF BLACK HAND

Writer: Geoff Johns | Artist: Doug Mahnke
ISBN: 978-1-4012-3767-7 | Diamond Code: JUL130229 | Price: $16.99 | Format: TP

Now teaming up with their former foe, Hal Jordan and Sinestro find themselves investigating a crime that leads them deep into the homeworld of the Indigo Tribe.

GREEN LANTERN VOL. 3: THE END

Writer: Geoff Johns | Artist: Doug Mahnke
ISBN: 978-1-4012-4744-7 | Diamond Code: JAN140338 | Price: $19.99 | Format: TP

Geoff Johns ends his monumental run on Green Lantern.

GREEN LANTERN VOL. 4: DARK DAYS

Writer: Robert Venditti | Artist: Billy Tan
ISBN: 978-1-4012-4744-7 | Diamond Code: DEC130303 | Price: $24.99 | Format: HC

New writer Robert Venditti creates an all-new direction with the new leader of the Green Lantern Corps: Hal Jordan!

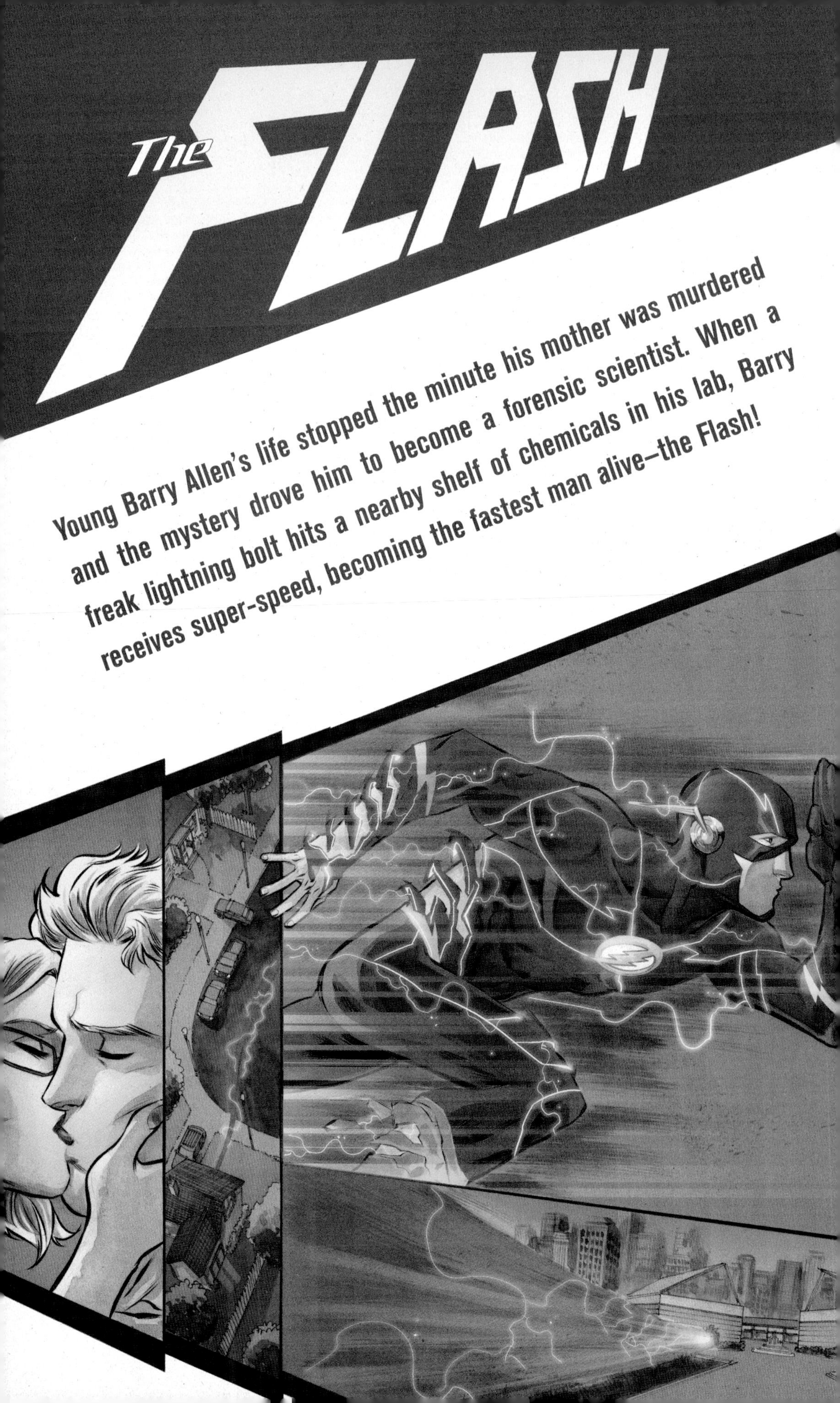
The FLASH
Young Barry Allen's life stopped the minute his mother was murdered and the mystery drove him to become a forensic scientist. When a freak lightning bolt hits a nearby shelf of chemicals in his lab, Barry receives super-speed, becoming the fastest man alive–the Flash!

THE FLASH: REBIRTH

Writer: Geoff Johns | Artist: Ethan Van Sciver

ISBN: 978-1-4012-3001-2 | Diamond Code: JAN110329 | Price: $14.99 | Format: TP

The explosive epic that reintroduces the newly returned Barry Allen as The Flash!

FLASHPOINT

Writer: Geoff Johns | Artist: Andy Kubert

ISBN: 978-1-4012-3338-9 | Diamond Code: DEC110276 | Price: $14.99 | Format: TP

Heroes become villains in an alternate universe tale that changed the DC Universe forever!

THE FLASH VOL. 1: MOVE FORWARD

Writers: Francis Manapul & Brian Buccellato | Artist: Francis Manapul

ISBN: 978-1-4012-3554-3 | Diamond Code: MAY130224 | Price: $16.99 | Format: TP

The Fastest Man Alive returns as Central City's greatest protector.

THE FLASH VOL. 2: ROGUES REVOLUTION

Writers: Francis Manapul & Brian Buccellato | Artist: Francis Manapul

ISBN: 978-1-4012-4273-2 | Diamond Code: NOV130229 | Price: $16.99 | Format: TP

The Flash's Rogue's Gallery is back, but the rogues are more powerful than ever and they're each looking to take down the Fastest Man Alive!

THE FLASH VOL. 3: GORILLA WARFARE

Writers: Francis Manapul & Brian Buccellato | Artist: Francis Manapul

ISBN: 978-1-4012-4274-9 | Diamond Code: OCT130243 | Price: $24.99 | Format: HC

The Flash will have to turn to his former enemies, the Rogues, if he wants defeat the invading hordes of Gorilla Grodd.

Oliver Queen had it all—movie star good looks, a matching cadre of women and his own billion dollar company. However, when the playboy became marooned on a desert island, he mastered the use of a bow and arrow to survive. Ollie eventually found his way back to his hometown, but with his priorities changed. Brandishing a new focus on bringing criminals to justice, he became the hero known as Green Arrow!

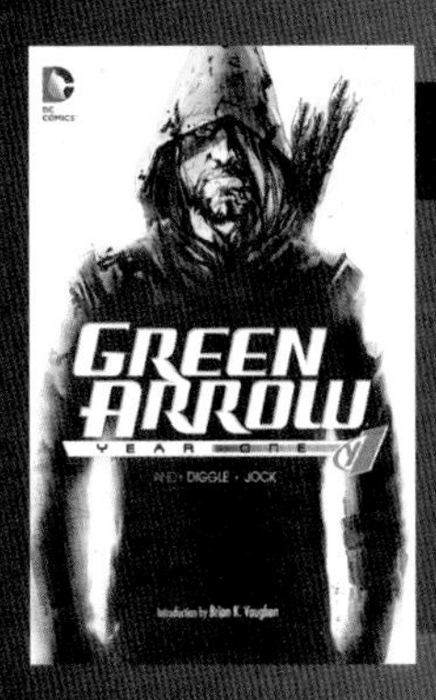

GREEN ARROW: YEAR ONE

Writer: Andy Diggle | Artist: Jock
ISBN: 978-14012-1743-3 | Diamond Code: JAN090227 | Price: $14.99 | Format: TP

Oliver's first year donning the quiver as Green Arrow!

GREEN ARROW: THE LONGBOW HUNTERS

Writer: Mike Grell | Artist: Mike Grell
ISBN: 978-1-4012-3862-9 | Diamond Code: JUN120250 | Price: $14.99 | Format: TP

A gritty take on a vigilante Emerald Archer in this essential Green Arrow story by Mike Grell.

FOR MATURE READERS

GREEN ARROW: THE ARCHER'S QUEST

Writer: Brad Meltzer | Artist: Phil Hester
ISBN: 978-1-4012-0044-2 | Diamond Code: JUN120251 | Price: $14.99 | Format: TP

Oliver Queen returns to discover secrets from his past, in this graphic novel by *New York Times* best-selling novelist Brad Meltzer.

GREEN ARROW VOL. 4: THE KILL MACHINE

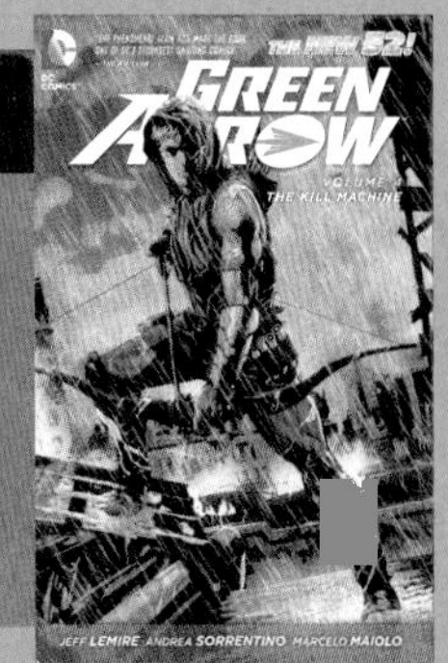

Writer: Jeff Lemire | Artist: Andrea Sorrentino
ISBN: 978-1-4012-4690-7 | Diamond Code: DEC130306 | Price: $16.99 | Format: TP

Jeff Lemire sets Green Arrow off in a bold new direction, starting with startling questions about Oliver's origin—involving his father?

ARROW VOL. 1

Writers: Marc Guggenheim & Andrew Kreisberg | Artist: Mike Grell
ISBN: 978-1-4012-4299-2 | Diamond Code: JUN130265 | Price: $16.99 | Format: TP

Spinning off directly from the hit CW television series ARROW come these digital-first adventures by show creators Andrew Kreisberg and Marc Guggenheim.

JUSTICE
LEAGUE

The World's Greatest Super Heroes: Superman, Batman, Wonder Woman, Green Lantern, The Flash, Aquaman, and Cyborg. Greater than the sum of their awe-inspiring parts, the Justice League handles threats too massive for any single hero.

JLA VOL. 1

Writer: Grant Morrison | Artists: Howard Porter & Oscar Jimenez
ISBN: 978-1-4012-3314-3 | Diamond Code: JUN110276 | Price: $19.99 | Format: TP

Grant Morrison relaunches the greatest team in the DC Universe—returning the powerhouse lineup of Superman, Batman, Wonder Woman, The Flash, Green Lantern, Aquaman and Martian Manhunter!

JLA: EARTH 2

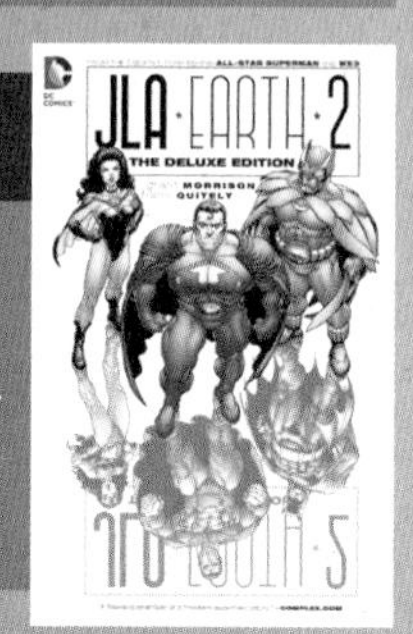

Writer: Grant Morrison | Artist: Frank Quitely
ISBN: 978-1-4012-4095-0 | Diamond Code: AUG120253 | Price: $14.99 | Format: TP

The Justice League battles its Earth 2 counterparts: the evil Crime Syndicate of Amerika!

IDENTITY CRISIS

Writer: Brad Meltzer | Artist: Rags Morales
ISBN: 978-1-4012-0458-7 | Diamond Code: AUG118125 | Price: $17.99 | Format: TP

Uncover the DC Universe's deadliest secret in this acclaimed miniseries from *New York Times* best-selling novelist Brad Meltzer.

FINAL CRISIS

Writer: Grant Morrison | Artists: J.G. Jones, Doug Mahnke and Carlos Pacheco
ISBN: 978-1-4012-4517-7 | Diamond Code: JAN140352 | Price: $19.99 | Format: TP

Grant Morrison takes the DC Universe on a battle through the multiverse that will leave both hero and villain changed forever.

JUSTICE LEAGUE VOL 1: ORIGIN

Writer: Geoff Johns | Artist: Jim Lee
ISBN: 978-1-4012-3788-2 | Diamond Code: OCT120252 | Price: $16.99 | Format: TP

In one of the most game-changing titles in comic industry history, Geoff Johns and Jim Lee re-imagine the Justice League for the 21st century.

JUSTICE LEAGUE VOL. 2: THE VILLAIN'S JOURNEY

Writer: Geoff Johns | Artist: Jim Lee
ISBN: 978-1-4012-3765-3 | Diamond Code: JUN130261 | Price: $16.99 | Format: TP

A villain from the League's past reemerges and it all ends with one of the most surprising moments in DC history!

JUSTICE LEAGUE VOL. 3: THRONE OF ATLANTIS

Writer: Geoff Johns | Artists: Ivan Reis & Paul Pelletier

ISBN: 978-1-4012-4698-3 | Diamond Code: JAN140339 | Price: $16.99 | Format: TP

The armies of Atlantis attack the surface world pitting the Justice League against one of their own.

JUSTICE LEAGUE VOL. 4: THE GRID

Writer: Geoff Johns | Artists: Ivan Reis

ISBN: 978-1-4012-4717-1 | Diamond Code: DEC130297 | Price: $24.99 | Format: HC

The Justice League becomes embroiled in a battle with the two other Justice Leagues—the Trinity War. But who is the real force behind it all?

JUSTICE LEAGUE: TRINITY WAR

Writers: Geoff Johns & Jeff Lemire | Artists: Ivan Reis, Doug Mahnke & Mikel Janin

ISBN: 978-1-4012-4519-1 | Diamond Code: NOV130226 | Price: $29.99 | Format: HC

The Justice League, Justice League Dark and Justice League of America go to war with one another, with the fate of the universe on the line.

DC: THE NEW FRONTIER VOL. 1

Writer: Darwyn Cooke | Artist: Darwyn Cooke

ISBN: 978-1-4012-0350-4 | Diamond Code: FEB058027 | Price: $19.99 | Format: TP

Darwyn Cooke's acclaimed journey from the end of the Golden Age to the genesis of a bold new heroic era in the late 1950s!

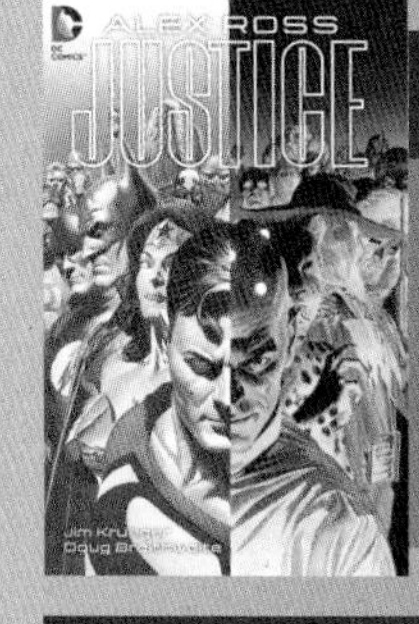

JUSTICE

Writers: Alex Ross & Jim Krueger | Artists: Alex Ross & Doug Braithwaite

ISBN: 978-1-4012-3526-0 | Diamond Code: MAR120254 | Price: $29.99 | Format: TP

The world's deadliest super villains band together to ... save the world? The Justice League must discover what's at the bottom of this mystery in Alex Ross's superb graphic novel.

KINGDOM COME

Writer: Mark Waid | Artist: Alex Ross

ISBN: 978-1-4012-2034-1 | Diamond Code: SEP138294 | Price: $19.99 | Format: TP

The unforgettable, best-selling miniseries from acclaimed writer Mark Waid and superstar painter Alex Ross that pits new and old eras of heroes against each other.

In a field dominated by male superheroes, Wonder Woman still emerges as one of the greatest of the genre. She is Princess Diana of the immortal Amazons from Greek mythology, with powers granted by the Gods of Olympus. The complete package of brains, beauty, and brawn, this warrior princess is worthy of her status as a pop culture icon.

WONDER WOMAN VOL. 1: BLOOD

Writer: Brian Azzarello | Artists: Cliff Chiang & Tony Akins
ISBN: 978-1-4012-3562-8 | Diamond Code: OCT120256 | Price: $14.99 | Format: TP

Superheroics and ancient myth meet, as critically acclaimed writer Brian Azzarello teams with Cliff Chiang and Tony Akins to begin a new chapter for the Amazon Princess.

WONDER WOMAN VOL. 2: GUTS

Writer: Brian Azzarello | Artists: Cliff Chiang & Tony Akins
ISBN: 978-1-4012-3810-0 | Diamond Code: JUN130271 | Price: $14.99 | Format: TP

Wonder Woman goes to hell! After playing Poseidon, Hades, and Hera against each other, Hades strikes back by kidnapping Zola and trapping her in the Underworld.

WONDER WOMAN VOL. 3: IRON

Writer: Brian Azzarello | Artists: Cliff Chiang & Tony Akins
ISBN: 978-1-4012-4607-5 | Diamond Code: MAY130226 | Price: $16.99 | Format: TP

As Wonder Woman digs deeper into her familial tree, she finds there are as many Gods that are willing to lend her a hand as there are those that would do her harm.

WONDER WOMAN VOL. 4: WAR

Writer: Brian Azzarello | Artists: Cliff Chiang & Tony Akins
ISBN: 978-1-4012-4608-2 | Diamond Code: NOV130234 | Price: $22.99 | Format: HC

Meet the new God of War: Wonder Woman!

WONDER WOMAN: ODYSSEY VOL. 1

Writers: J. Michael Straczynski & Phil Hester | Artists: Don Kramer, Eduardo Pansica & others
ISBN: 978-1-4012-3078-4 | Diamond Code: APR120258 | Price: $14.99 | Format: TP

If you think you knew who Wonder Woman was—think again! All bets are off in this all-new direction for the long-running series that's perfect for new readers!

WONDER WOMAN: ODYSSEY VOL. 2

Writers: J. Michael Straczynski & Phil Hester | Artists: Don Kramer, Eduardo Pansica & others
ISBN: 978-1-4012-3432-4 | Diamond Code: NOV120274 | Price: $14.99 | Format: TP

Diana, a.k.a. Wonder Woman, must track down the truth behind who or what destroyed Paradise Island.

TEEN TITANS

Robin. Superboy. Kid Flash. Wonder Girl. They're the protégés of the World's Greatest Superheroes, but they are first and foremost an extended family of friends. They help each other cope with the pressure of being the most powerful adolescents on the planet as they face off against super-villains, super-calamities, and sometimes even super-hormones.

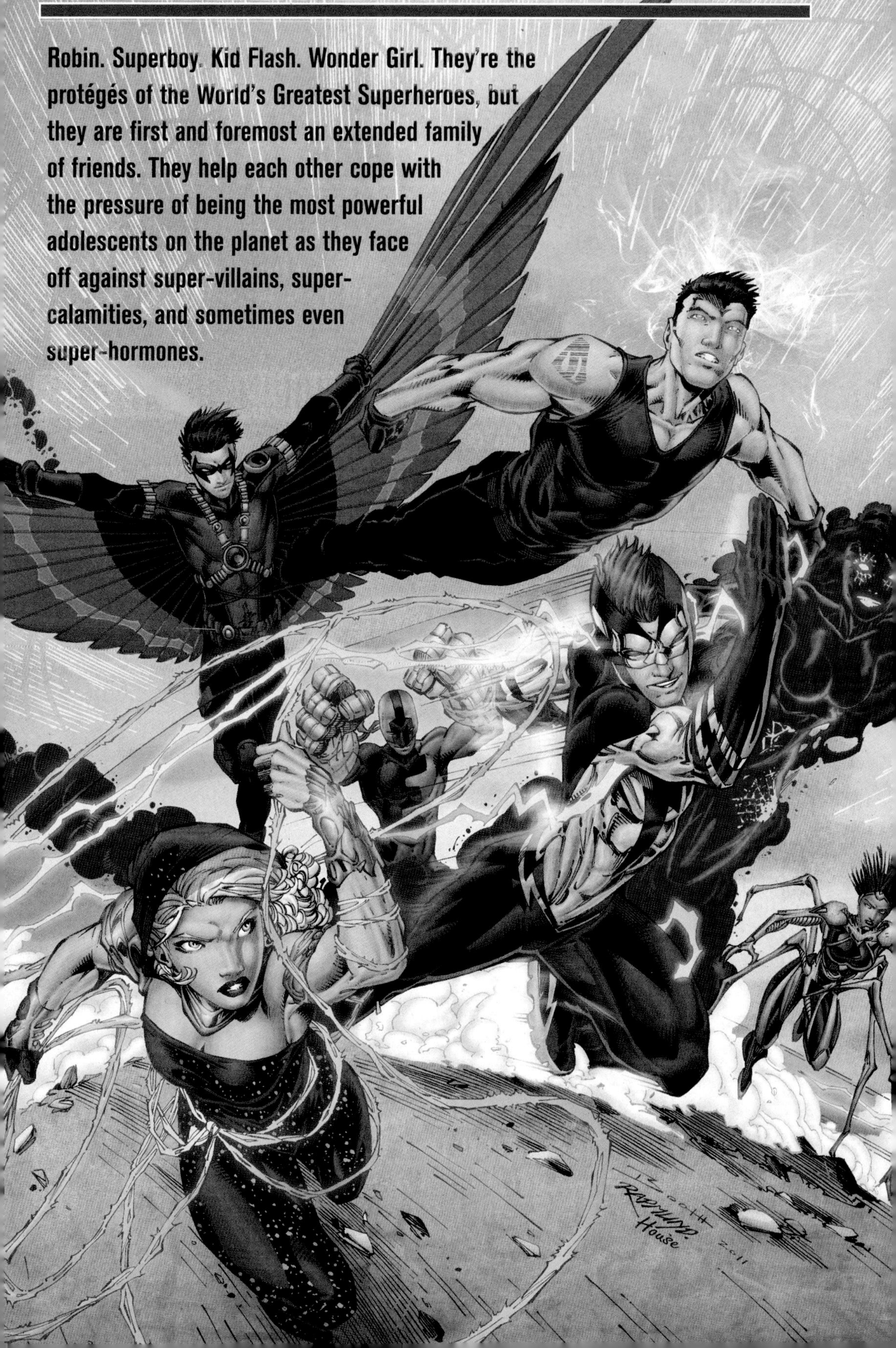

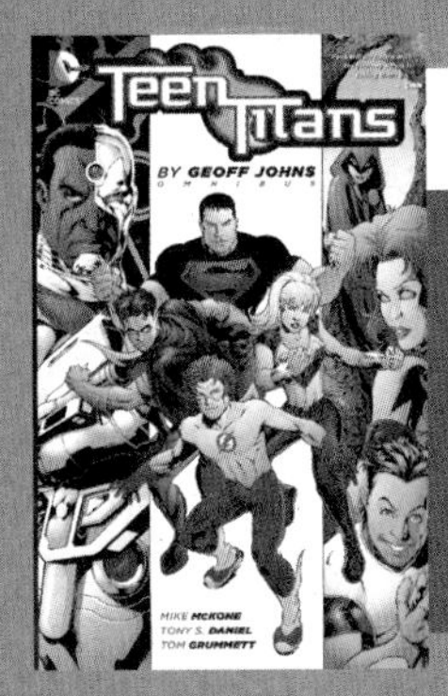

TEEN TITANS BY GEOFF JOHNS OMNIBUS

Writer: Geoff Johns | Artist: Various
ISBN: 978-1-4012-3693-9 | Diamond Code: SEP120242 | Price: $150.00 | Format: HC

Award-winning, *New York Times* best-selling writer Geoff Johns' celebrated *Teen Titans* run collected into one giant hardcover tome!

TEEN TITANS VOL. 1: IT'S OUR RIGHT TO FIGHT

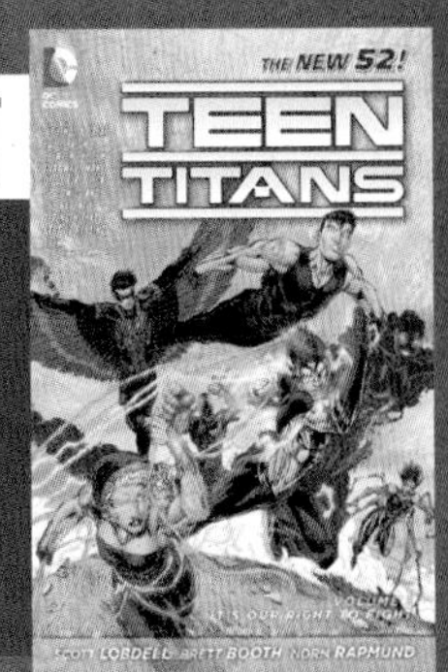

Writer: Scott Lobdell | Artist: Brett Booth
ISBN: 978-1-4012-3698-4 | Diamond Code: JUN120239 | Price: $14.99 | Format: TP

Scott Lobdell and Brett Booth launch an all-new Teen Titans into new and action-packed adventures!

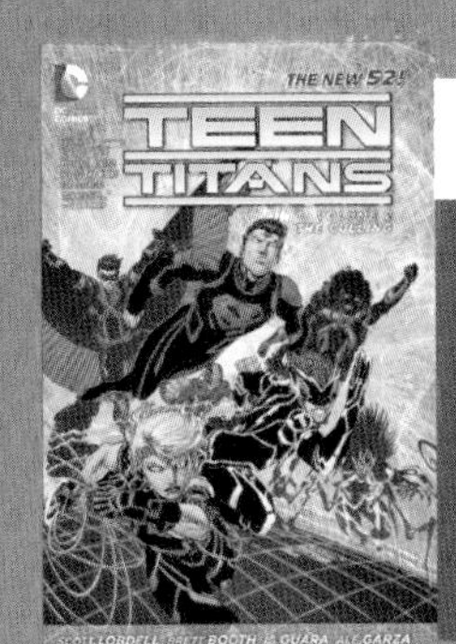

TEEN TITANS VOL. 2: THE CULLING

Writer: Scott Lobdell | Artist: Brett Booth
ISBN: 978-1-4012-4103-2 | Diamond Code: MAR130272 | Price: $16.99 | Format: TP

The organization known as N.O.W.H.E.R.E. captures Superboy, the Teen Titans, and Legion Lost and pits the young heroes against each other to weed out the weak.

THE CULLING: RISE OF THE RAVAGERS

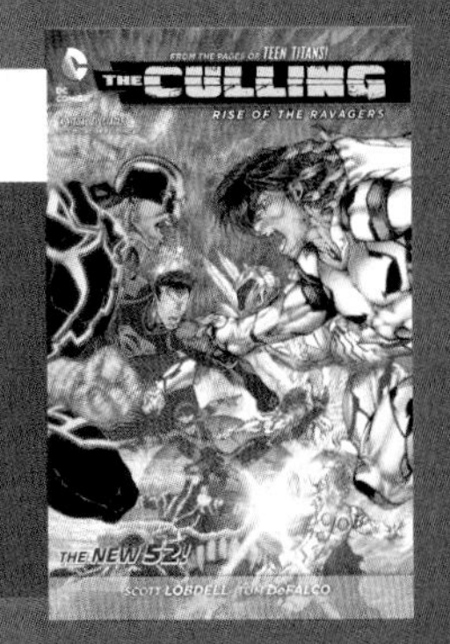

Writers: Tom Defalco & Scott Lobdell | Artists: Various
ISBN: 978-1-4012-3799-8 | Diamond Code: OCT120250 | Price: $16.99 | Format: TP

The Teen Titans and the teen heroes from *Legion Lost* are trapped in a deadly arena where they must fight each other to the death!

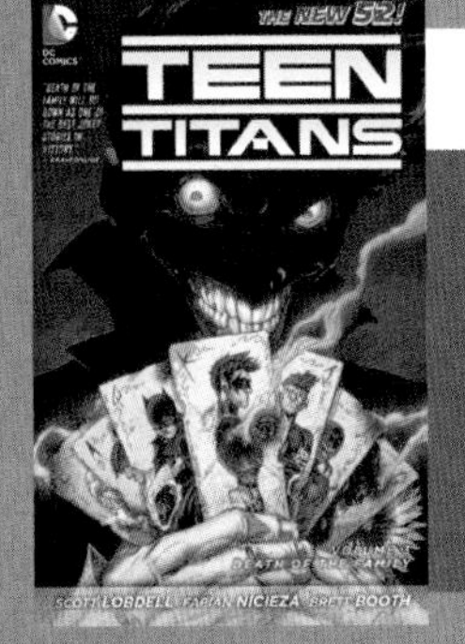

TEEN TITANS VOL. 3: DEATH OF THE FAMILY

Writers: Scott Lobdell & Fabian Nicieza | Artist: Brett Booth
ISBN: 978-1-4012-4321-0 | Diamond Code: SEP130274 | Price: $14.99 | Format: TP

The team is finally reunited in the wake of "Death of the Family," but something is very wrong with Red Robin! What did The Joker do?

DIGITAL-FIRST COMICS

Every day is new comics day with our Digital-First line. Whether you want a fresh take on your favorite character, to see the cutest versions of Gotham City's finest, or you just miss SMALLVILLE, there's something here for everybody.

ADVENTURES OF SUPERMAN VOL. 1

Writers: Michael Avon Oeming, Jeff Parker, Jeff Lemire & others
Artists: Pia Guerra, Chris Samnee & others
ISBN: 978-1-4012-4688-4 | Diamond Code: JAN140346 | Price: $14.99 | Format: TP

The best creators in comics take on the Man of Steel in this collection of stand-alone Superman stories!

ARROW VOL. 1

Writers: Marc Guggenheim & Andrew Kreisberg | Artist: Mike Grell
ISBN: 978-1-4012-42992 | Diamond Code: JUN130265 | Price: $16.99 | Format: TP

Spinning off directly from the hit CW television series *Arrow* come these digital-first adventures by show creators Andrew Kreisberg and Marc Guggenheim.

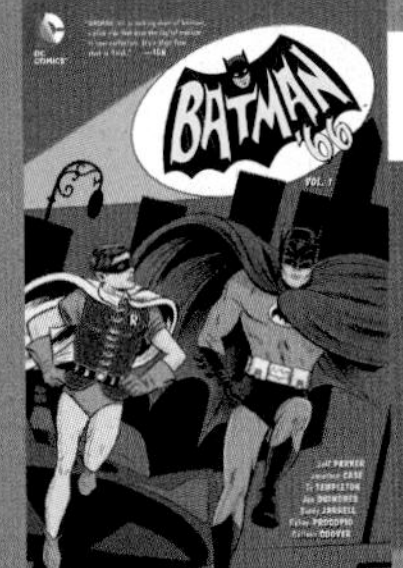

BATMAN '66 VOL. 1

Writer: Jeff Parker | Artists: Various

ISBN: 978-1-4012-4721-8 | Diamond Code: DEC130307 | Price: $19.99 | Format: HC

Put on your go-go boots and get ready to "Batusi" back to the Swingin' 60s as DC Comics reimagines the classic Batman TV series in comics form for the first time!

BATMAN: LI'L GOTHAM VOL. 1

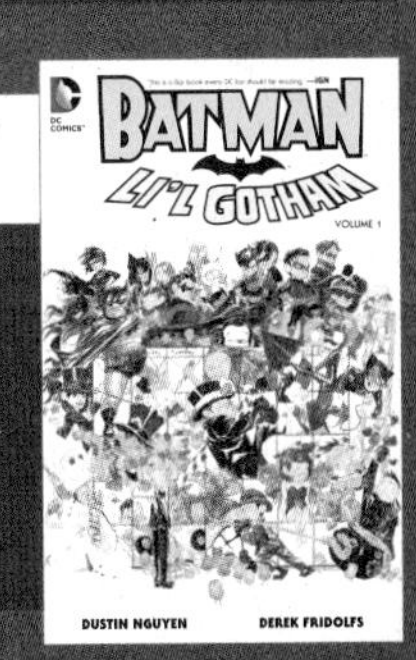

Writer: Derek Fridolfs & Dustin Nguyen | Artist: Dustin Nguyen

ISBN: 978-1-4012-4494-1 | Diamond Code: NOV130255 | Price: $12.99 | Format: TP

Follow all of your favorite Gotham City characters throughout each holiday in these gorgeously drawn and painted all-ages tales!

BATMAN BEYOND: 10,000 CLOWNS

Writer: Adam Beechen | Artist: Norm Breyfogle

ISBN: 978-1-4012-4034-9 | Diamond Code: FEB130221 | Price: $16.99 | Format: TP

When the Jokerz gang launches a series of coordinated attacks all around the town, Terry can only save so many people at once. Who can Terry turn to for help?

INJUSTICE: GODS AMONG US VOL. 1

Writer: Tom Taylor | Artists: Jheremy Raapack & Mike S. Miller

ISBN: 978-1-4012-4500-9 | Diamond Code: JUL130242 | Price: $19.99 | Format: HC

After the most unimaginable tragedy strikes Superman, he decides that the Justice League must take a more active stance against evil. The only man to stand in his way? Batman! The blockbuster video game phenomenon comes to the comic book page!

JUSTICE LEAGUE BEYOND: KONSTRICTION

Writers: Derek Fridolfs & Dustin Nguyen | Artist: Dustin Nguyen

ISBN: 978-1-4012-4023-3 | Diamond Code: FEB130222 | Price: $16.99 | Format: TP

Batman is a new recruit in the mighty Justice League, but the team will be immediately tested by a very Neo Gotham-related enemy. How will they work together to combat this threat?

SMALLVILLE SEASON 11 VOL 1: GUARDIAN

Writer: Bryan Q. Miller | Artists: Pere Perez

ISBN: 978-1-4012-3824-7 | Diamond Code: JAN130314 | Price: $14.99 | Format: TP

Picking up six months after *Smallville Season 10*, *Season 11* explores Clark's understanding of the true power of his Superman identity.

VERTIGO
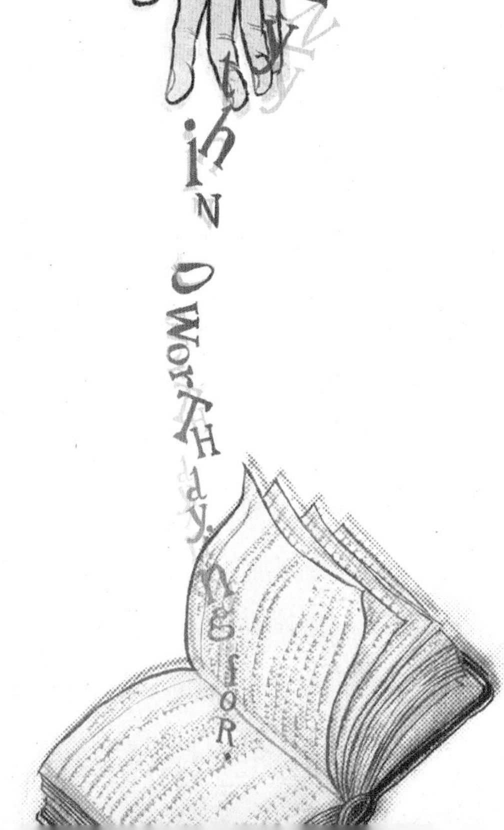

ESSENTIALS

100 BULLETS VOL. 1: FIRST SHOT, LAST CALL

Writer: Brian Azzarello | Artist: Eduardo Risso

ISBN: 978-1-5638-9645-3 | Diamond Code: JAN128095 | Price: $12.99 | Format: TP

Guaranteed full immunity, what would you do? Vertigo's seminal crime series features ordinary citizens who are given the opportunity to exact revenge on a person who has wronged them.

DAYTRIPPER

Writer: Gabriel Bá | Artist: Fábio Moon

ISBN: 978-1-4012-2969-6 | Diamond Code: NOV100268 | Price: $19.99 | Format: TP

This award-winning graphic novel follows Bras de Olivias Dominguez during different periods in his life, each with the same ending: his death.

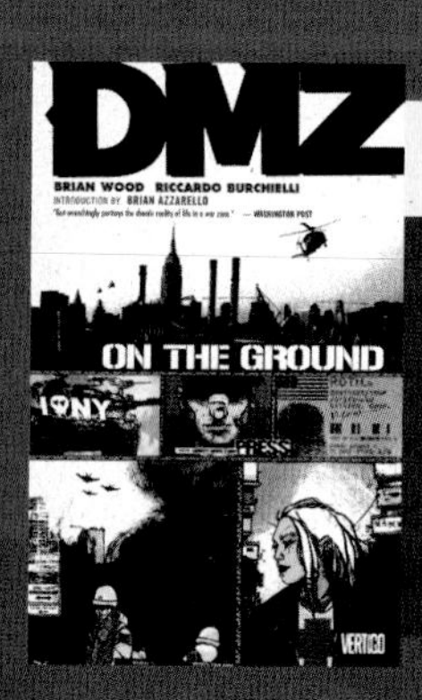

DMZ VOL. 1: ON THE GROUND

Writer: Brian Wood | Artist: Riccardo Burchielli

ISBN: 978-1-4012-1062-5 | Diamond Code: OCT118125 | Price: $12.99 | Format: TP

In the near future after a second American Civil War, Manhattan becomes a wasteland known as the DMZ. Matty Roth, a naïve aspiring photojournalist, must cover the war zone from the inside ... if he can survive.

EX MACHINA BOOK ONE

Writer: Brian K. Vaughan | Artist: Tony Harris

ISBN: 978-1-4012-4498-9 | Diamond Code: OCT130291 | Price: $19.99 | Format: TP

Tired of risking his life day-in and day-out, superhero Mitchell Hundred becomes the Mayor of New York City in this thrilling graphic novel from the creator of *Y: The Last Man*.

THE GIRL WITH THE DRAGON TATTOO

Writer: Denise Mina | Artists: Leonardo Manco & Andrea Mutti

ISBN: 978-1-4012-4286-2 | Diamond Code: JAN140369 | Price: $24.99 | Format: TP

A graphic novel adaptation of the #1 international bestseller and box office smash hit.

iZOMBIE VOL. 1: DEAD TO THE WORLD

Writer: Chris Roberson | Artist: Mike Allred
ISBN: 978-1-4012-2965-8 | Diamond Code: DEC100299 | Price: $14.99 | Format: TP

The everyday stories of twenty-something zombie Gwen Dylan, as she makes her way along in this living world.

JOHN CONSTANTINE, HELLBLAZER VOL 1: ORIGINAL SINS

Writer: Jamie Delano | Artists: John Ridgway, Alfredo Alcala & Rick Veitch
ISBN: 978-1-4012-3006-7 | Diamond Code: DEC100302 | Price: $19.99 | Format: TP

Vertigo's longest-running series featuring the antihero, John Constantine, England's chain-smoking, low-rent magician.

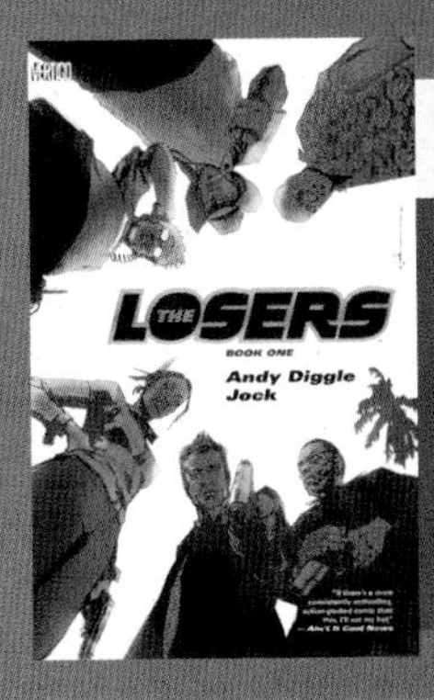

THE LOSERS BOOK ONE

Writer: Andy Diggle | Artist: Jock
ISBN: 978-1-4012-2733-3 | Diamond Code: NOV090232 | Price: $19.99 | Format: TP

A team of former elite U.S. Special Forces soldiers, the Losers, hunts down the government forces that betrayed them.

PREACHER BOOK ONE

Writer: Garth Ennis | Artist: Steve Dillon
ISBN: 978-1-4012-4045-5 | Diamond Code: MAR130303 | Price: $19.99 | Format: TP

Jesse Custer, a wayward preacher begins a violent journey to find God (literally), joined by his girlfriend Tulip and the hard-drinking Irish vampire Cassidy.

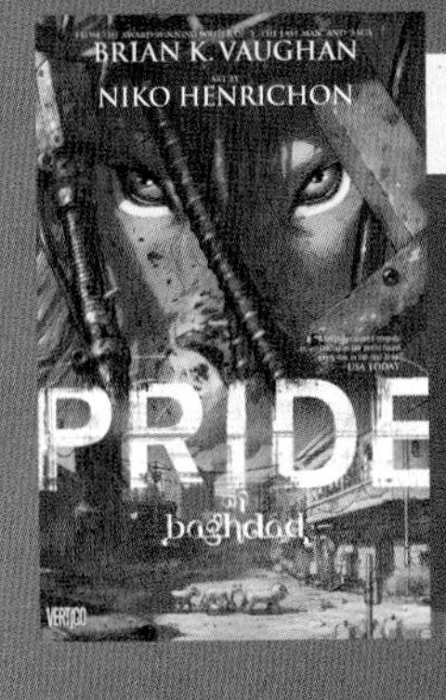

PRIDE OF BAGHDAD

Writer: Brian K. Vaughan | Artist: Nico Henrichon
ISBN: 978-1-4012-0315-3 | Diamond Code: FEB118119 | Price: $14.99 | Format: TP

From the writer of *Y: The Last Man* and *Ex Machina*, this standalone graphic novel tells the real-life story of a pride of lions that escape a Baghdad zoo during the Iraq War of 2003 in a touching allegory of the real meaning of freedom.

PUNK ROCK JESUS

Writer: Sean Murphy | Artist: Sean Murphy
ISBN: 978-1-4012-3768-4 | Diamond Code: JAN130330 | Price: $16.99 | Format: TP

A reality TV show starring a clone of Jesus Christ causes chaos across the U.S. of the near future in *Punk Rock Jesus*, a new graphic novel written and drawn by Sean Murphy.

SCALPED VOL. 1: INDIAN COUNTRY

Writer: Jason Aaron | Artist: R.M. Guera
ISBN: 978-1-4012-1317-6 | Diamond Code: APR108251 | Price: $14.99 | Format: TP

Dashiell Bad Horse must return to the reservation he grew up in, determined to clean up the crime-ridden "Rez" he left years ago, one way or another.

SWEET TOOTH VOL. 1: OUT OF THE DEEP WOODS

Writer: Jeff Lemire | Artist: Jeff Lemire
ISBN: 978-1-4012-2696-1 | Diamond Code: AUG108007 | Price: $12.99 | Format: TP

Gus—a boy born with deer-like antlers—is left to survive in an American landscape devastated a decade earlier by an inexplicable pandemic.

TRANSMETROPOLITAN VOL. 1: BACK ON THE STREET

Writer: Warren Ellis | Artist: Darick Robertson
ISBN: 978-1-4012-2084-6 | Diamond Code: DEC080220 | Price: $14.99 | Format: TP

Mastermind writer Warren Ellis delivers this sharp, manic, anything-goes exploration of urban life about journalist/cult author Spider Jerusalem.

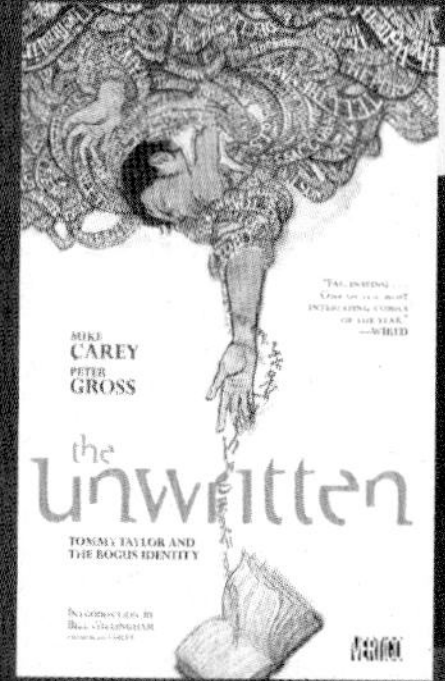

THE UNWRITTEN VOL. 1: TOMMY TAYLOR AND THE BOGUS IDENTITY

Writer: Mike Carey | Artist: Peter Gross
ISBN: 978-1-4012-2565-0 | Diamond Code: APR128238 | Price: $14.99 | Format: TP

Tom Taylor, the inspiration for the boy wizard from the series of novels his father made famous, finds that the worlds of fiction and real life are crossing over into each other in this fantastic graphic novel.

One of the most popular and critically acclaimed graphic novel series of all time, Neil Gaiman's award-winning masterpiece THE SANDMAN has set the standard for mature, lyrical fantasy in the comic book field. Illustrated by a rotating cast of the medium's most sought-after artists, the series is a rich blend of modern and ancient mythology into which contemporary fiction, historical drama and legend are seamlessly interwoven.

NEIL GAIMAN's

SANDMAN

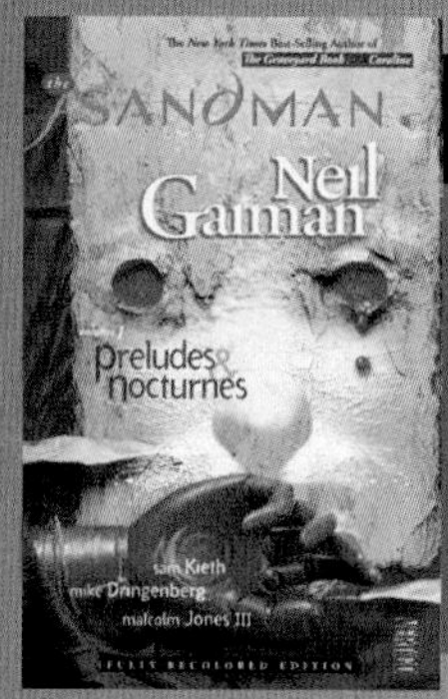

THE SANDMAN VOL. 1: PRELUDES & NOCTURNES

Writer: Neil Gaiman | Artists: Mike Dringenberg, Sam Kieth & Malcolm Jones III
ISBN: 978-1-4012-2575-9 | Diamond Code: JUL100259 | Price: $19.99 | Format: TP

Collects issues #1-8.

THE SANDMAN VOL. 2: THE DOLL'S HOUSE

Writer: Neil Gaiman
Artists: Mike Dringenberg, Sam Kieth, Malcolm Jones III, Chris Bachalo & Michael Zulli
ISBN: 978-1-4012-2799-9 | Diamond Code: JUL100260 | Price: $19.99 | Format: TP

Collects issues #9-16.

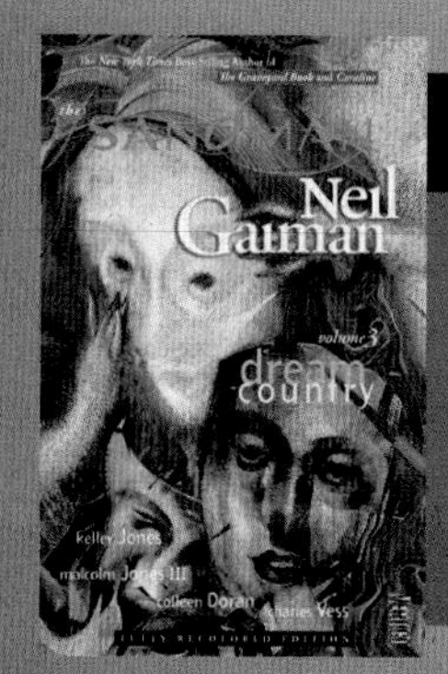

THE SANDMAN VOL. 3: DREAM COUNTRY

Writer: Neil Gaiman
Artists: Mike Dringenberg, Kelley Jones, Malcolm Jones III, Colleen Doran & Charles Vess
ISBN: 978-1-4012-2935-1 | Diamond Code: JUL100261 | Price: $19.99 | Format: TP

Collects issues #17-20.

THE SANDMAN VOL. 4: SEASON OF MISTS

Writer: Neil Gaiman
Artists: Kelley Jones, Malcolm Jones III, P. Craig Russell & Matt Wagner
ISBN: 978-1-4012-3042-5 | Diamond Code: OCT100330 | Price: $19.99 | Format: TP

Collects issues #21-28.

THE SANDMAN VOL. 5: A GAME OF YOU

Writer: Neil Gaiman
Artists: Shawn McManus, Colleen Doran, Stan Woch, Bryan Talbot & others
ISBN: 978-1-4012-3043-2 | Diamond Code: JAN110431 | Price: $19.99 | Format: TP

Collects issues #32-37.

THE SANDMAN VOL. 6: FABLES & REFLECTIONS

Writer: Neil Gaiman
Artists: Shawn McManus, P. Craig Russell, Stan Woch, Bryan Talbot, Jill Thompson & others
ISBN: 978-1-4012-3123-1 | Diamond Code: MAY110297 | Price: $19.99 | Format: TP

Collects issues #29-31, #38-40 and #50.

THE SANDMAN VOL. 7: BRIEF LIVES

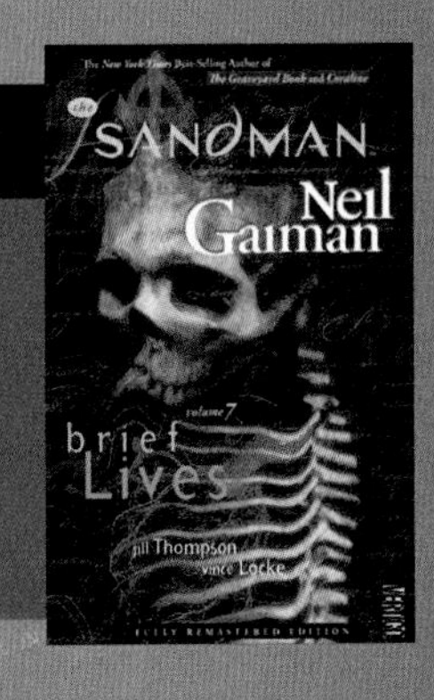

Writer: Neil Gaiman | Artist: Jill Thompson & Vince Locke
ISBN: 978-1-4012-3263-4 | Diamond Code: SEP110177 | Price: $19.99 | Format: TP

Collects issues #41-49.

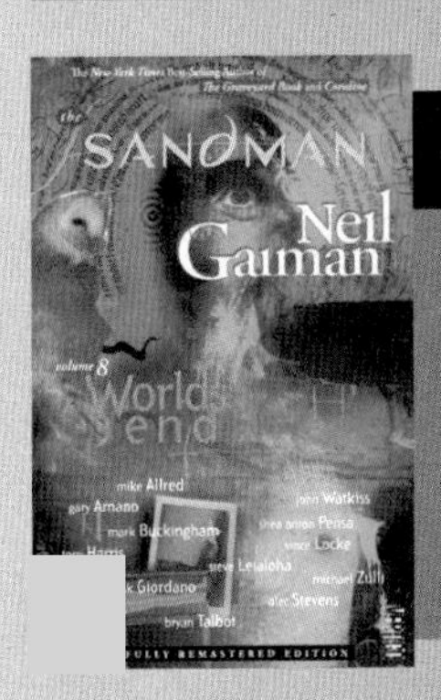

THE SANDMAN VOL. 8: WORLDS' END

Writer: Neil Gaiman
Artists: Mike Allred, Mark Buckingham, Michael Zulli, Tony Harris & others
ISBN: 978-1-4012-3402-7 | Diamond Code: NOV110233 | Price: $19.99 | Format: TP

Collects issues #51-56.

THE SANDMAN VOL. 9: THE KINDLY ONES

Writer: Neil Gaiman
Artists: Marc Hempel, Richard Case, Charles Vess, Kevin Nowlan & others
ISBN: 978-1-4012-3545-1 | Diamond Code: FEB120298 | Price: $19.99 | Format: TP

Collects issues #57-69 and *Vertigo Jam* #1.

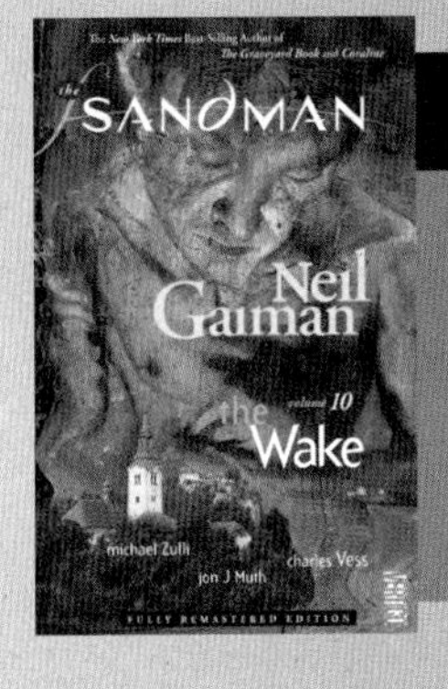

THE SANDMAN VOL. 10: THE WAKE

Writer: Neil Gaiman | Artists: Michael Zulli, Charles Vess & Jon J Muth
ISBN: 978-1-4012-3754-7 | Diamond Code: AUG120292 | Price: $19.99 | Format: TP

Collects issues #70-75.

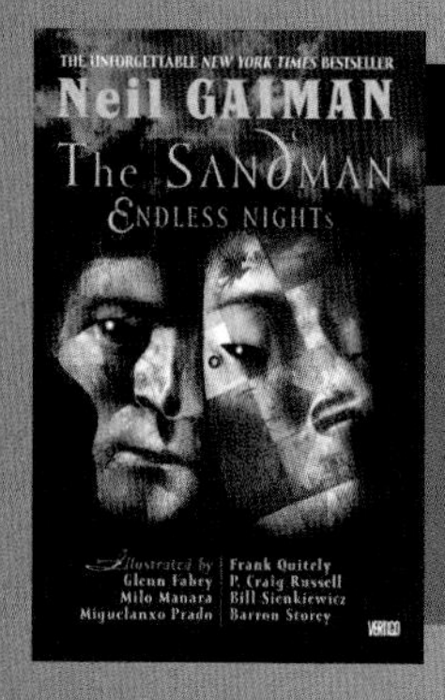

THE SANDMAN: ENDLESS NIGHTS

Writer: Neil Gaiman
Artists: Frank Quitely, Glenn Fabry, Bill Sienkiewicz, P. Craig Russell & others
ISBN: 978-1-4012-0113-5 | Diamond Code: DEC068187 | Price: $19.99 | Format: TP

Seven stories featuring the Sandman and his siblings, the Endless, with art from the industry's finest illustrators.

THE SANDMAN: THE DREAM HUNTERS

Writer: Neil Gaiman | Artist: Yoshitaka Amano
ISBN: 978-1-5638-9629-3 | Diamond Code: DEC068030 | Price: $19.99 | Format: TP

A novella with stunning art from Japanese artist Yoshitaka Amano.

THE SANDMAN: THE DREAM HUNTERS

Writer: Neil Gaiman | Artist: P. Craig Russell
ISBN: 978-1-4912-2428-8 | Diamond Code: JUN100280 | Price: $19.99 | Format: TP

P. Craig Russell's traditional comic book adaptation of the breakthrough original graphic novel.

DEATH

Writer: Neil Gaiman | Artists: Various
ISBN: 978-1-4012-4716-4 | Diamond Code: DEC130341 | Price: $19.99 | Format: TP

Vertigo's Death stories are all captured here in one graphic novel.

LUCIFER: BOOK ONE

Writer: Mike Carey | Artists: Peter Gross, Ryan Kelly, Dean Ormston & others
ISBN: 978-1-4012-4026-4 | Diamond Code: FEB130247 | Price: $29.99 | Format: TP

Lucifer Morningstar, the fallen angel, steps out of the pages of Neil Gaiman's THE SANDMAN and stars in his own series from the creative team behind THE UNWRITTEN.

Bill Willingham's
FABLES
Run out of their happily-ever-after homeworlds by a mighty conqueror known only as The Adversary, these universally recognized princes, princesses, talking animals, heroes, and villains now face a new challenge: adapting to a modern-day Manhattan filled with sex, violence, and lots of moral ambiguity.

FABLES VOL. 1: LEGENDS IN EXILE

Writer: Bill Willingham | Artist: Lan Medina
ISBN: 978-1-4012-3755-4 | Diamond Code: FEB120285 | Price: $12.99 | Format: TP

Collects issues #1-5.

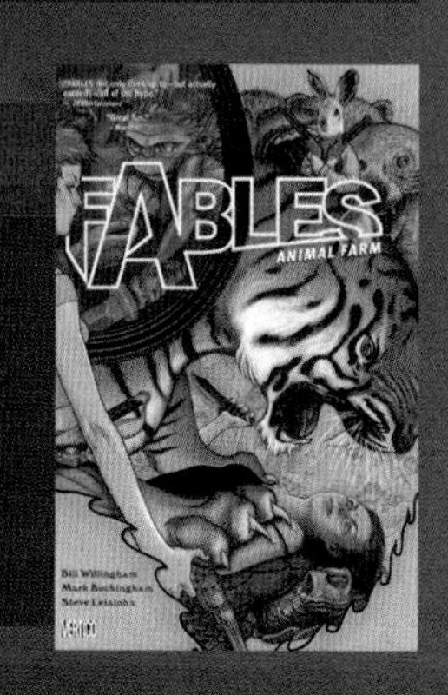

FABLES VOL. 2: ANIMAL FARM

Writer: Bill Willingham | Artist: Mark Buckingham
ISBN: 978-1-4012-0077-0 | Diamond Code: MAR058123 | Price: $14.99 | Format: TP

Collects issues #6-10.

FABLES VOL. 3: STORYBOOK LOVE

Writer: Bill Willingham | Artist: Mark Buckingham
ISBN: 978-1-4012-0256-9 | Diamond Code: JAN128247 | Price: $17.99 | Format: TP

Collects issues #11-18.

FABLES VOL. 4: MARCH OF THE WOODEN SOLDIERS

Writer: Bill Willingham | Artist: Mark Buckingham
ISBN: 978-1-4012-0222-4 | Diamond Code: OCT058021 | Price: $17.99 | Format: TP

Collects issues #19-21 and #23-27.

FABLES VOL. 5: THE MEAN SEASONS

Writer: Bill Willingham | Artist: Mark Buckingham
ISBN: 978-1-4012-0486-0 | Diamond Code: JAN050373 | Price: $17.99 | Format: TP

Collects issues #22 and #28-33.

FABLES VOL. 6: HOMELANDS

Writer: Bill Willingham | Artist: Mark Buckingham
ISBN: 978-1-4012-0500-3 | Diamond Code: OCT050317 | Price: $14.99 | Format: TP

Collects issues #34-41.

FABLES VOL. 7: ARABIAN NIGHTS (AND DAYS)

Writer: Bill Willingham | Artist: Mark Buckingham
ISBN: 978-1-4012-1000-7 | Diamond Code: MAR060384 | Price: $14.99 | Format: TP

Collects issues #42-47.

FABLES VOL. 8: WOLVES

Writer: Bill Willingham | Artist: Mark Buckingham
ISBN: 978-1-4012-1001-4 | Diamond Code: SEP060313 | Price: $17.99 | Format: TP

Collects issues #48-51.

FABLES VOL. 9: SONS OF EMPIRE

Writer: Bill Willingham | Artist: Mark Buckingham
ISBN: 978-1-4012-1316-9 | Diamond Code: MAR070271 | Price: $17.99 | Format: TP

Collects issues #52-59.

FABLES VOL. 10: THE GOOD PRINCE

Writer: Bill Willingham | Artist: Mark Buckingham
ISBN: 978-1-4012-1686-3 | Diamond Code: FEB080297 | Price: $17.99 | Format: TP

Collects issues #60-69.

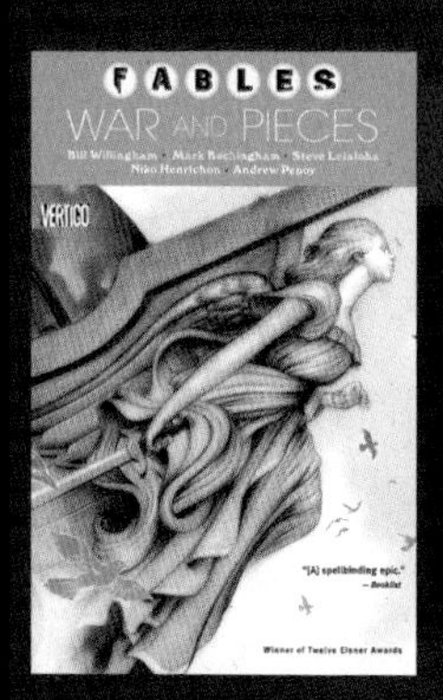

FABLES VOL. 11: WAR AND PIECES

Writer: Bill Willingham | Artist: Mark Buckingham
ISBN: 978-1-4012-1913-0 | Diamond Code: AUG080229 | Price: $17.99 | Format: TP

Collects issues #70-75.

FABLES VOL. 12: THE DARK AGES

Writer: Bill Willingham | Artist: Mark Buckingham
ISBN: 978-1-4012-2316-8 | Diamond Code: MAY090236 | Price: $17.99 | Format: TP

Collects issues #76-82.

FABLES VOL. 13: THE GREAT FABLES CROSSOVER

Writers: Bill Willingham & Matt Sturges | Artists: Mark Buckingham & Tony Akins
ISBN: 978-1-4012-2572-8 | Diamond Code: NOV090228 | Price: $17.99 | Format: TP

Collects issues #83-85, JACK OF FABLES #33-35 and THE LITERALS #1-3.

FABLES VOL. 14: WITCHES

Writer: Bill Willingham | Artist: Mark Buckingham
ISBN: 978-1-4012-2880-4 | Diamond Code: SEP100304 | Price: $17.99 | Format: TP

Collects issues #86-93.

FABLES VOL. 15: ROSE RED

Writer: Bill Willingham | Artist: Mark Buckingham
ISBN: 978-1-4012-3000-5 | Diamond Code: JAN110422 | Price: $17.99 | Format: TP

Collects issues #94-100.

FABLES VOL. 16: SUPER TEAM

Writer: Bill Willingham | Artist: Mark Buckingham
ISBN: 978-1-4012-3306-8 | Diamond Code: SEP110221 | Price: $14.99 | Format: TP
Collects issues #101-107.

FABLES VOL. 17: INHERIT THE WIND

Writer: Bill Willingham | Artist: Mark Buckingham
ISBN: 978-1-4012-3516-1 | Diamond Code: APR120282 | Price: $14.99 | Format: TP
Collects issues #108-113.

FABLES VOL. 18: CUBS IN TOYLAND

Writer: Bill Willingham | Artist: Mark Buckingham
ISBN: 978-1-4012-3769-1 | Diamond Code: OCT120296 | Price: $16.99 | Format: TP
Collects issues #114-123.

FABLES VOL. 19: SNOW WHITE

Writer: Bill Willingham | Artist: Mark Buckingham
ISBN: 978-1-4012-4248-0 | Diamond Code: SEP130305 | Price: $16.99 | Format: TP
Collects issues #124-129 and the back-up stories from #114-123.

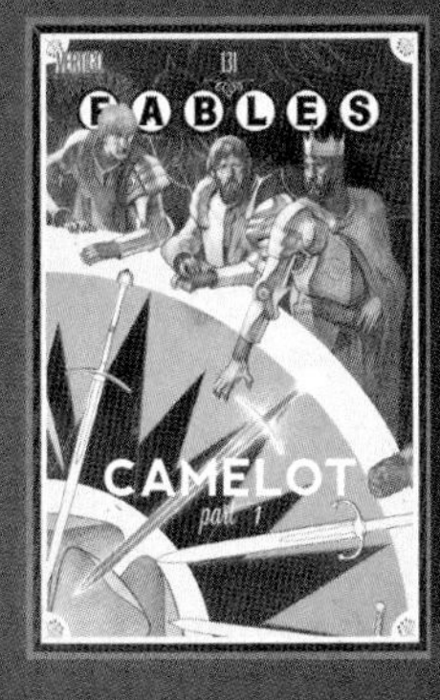

FABLES VOL. 20: CAMELOT

Writer: Bill Willingham | Artist: Mark Buckingham
ISBN: 978-1-4012-4516-0 | Diamond Code: SEP130305 | Price: $19.99 | Format: TP
Collects issues #131-136.

FABLES: 1001 NIGHTS OF SNOWFALL

Writer: Bill Willingham
Artists: Brian Bolland, Charles Vess, Jill Thompson, Mark Buckingham & others
ISBN: 978-1-4012-0369-6 | Diamond Code: DEC070297 | Price: $14.99 | Format: TP

Snow White charms a young sultan with untold tales of the citizens of Fabletown in this graphic novel anthology.

FABLES: WEREWOLVES OF THE HEARTLAND

Writer: Bill Willingham | Artists: Jim Fern & Craig Hamilton
ISBN: 978-1-4012-2480-6 | Diamond Code: JUL130260 | Price: $14.99 | Format: TP

Bigby Wolf travels across America on a quest for a new settlement for his fellow Fables, but finds himself caught in a small town of werewolves.

FABLES ENCYCLOPEDIA

Writers: Jess Nevins & Bill Willingham | Artists: Various
ISBN: 978-1-4012-4395-1 | Diamond Code: JUN130286 | Price: $39.99 | Format: HC

The histories behind the fairy tale characters in *New York Times* best-selling author Bill Willingham's series FABLES are uncovered here in the FABLES ENCYCLOPEDIA.

FAIREST VOL. 1: WIDE AWAKE

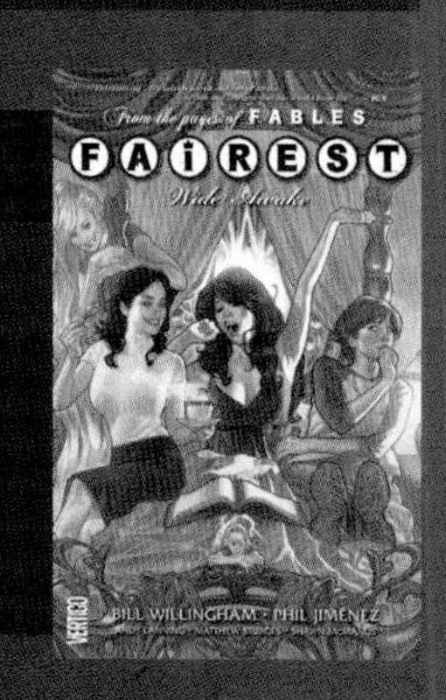

Writer: Bill Willingham | Artist: Phil Jimenez
ISBN: 978-1-4012-3550-5 | Diamond Code: AUG120283 | Price: $14.99 | Format: TP

The lovely and dangerous women of Fabletown get their own series.

FAIREST IN ALL THE LAND

Writer: Bill Willingham | Artist: Various
ISBN: 978-1-4012-3900-8 | Diamond Code: JUL130257 | Price: $22.99 | Format: HC

The best names in comics take their turns fleshing out the pasts of the loveliest Fables in existence!

In 2002, every man, boy and mammal with a Y chromosome dies during a worldwide epidemic. Every man except for one. Yorick Brown and his monkey Ampersand are the only two males to survive and commence a years-long odyssey to discover why. Writer Brian K. Vaughan and artist Pia Guerra bring to vivid life the age-old speculation: What would really happen to the last man on Earth?

Brian K. Vaughan's

THE LAST MAN

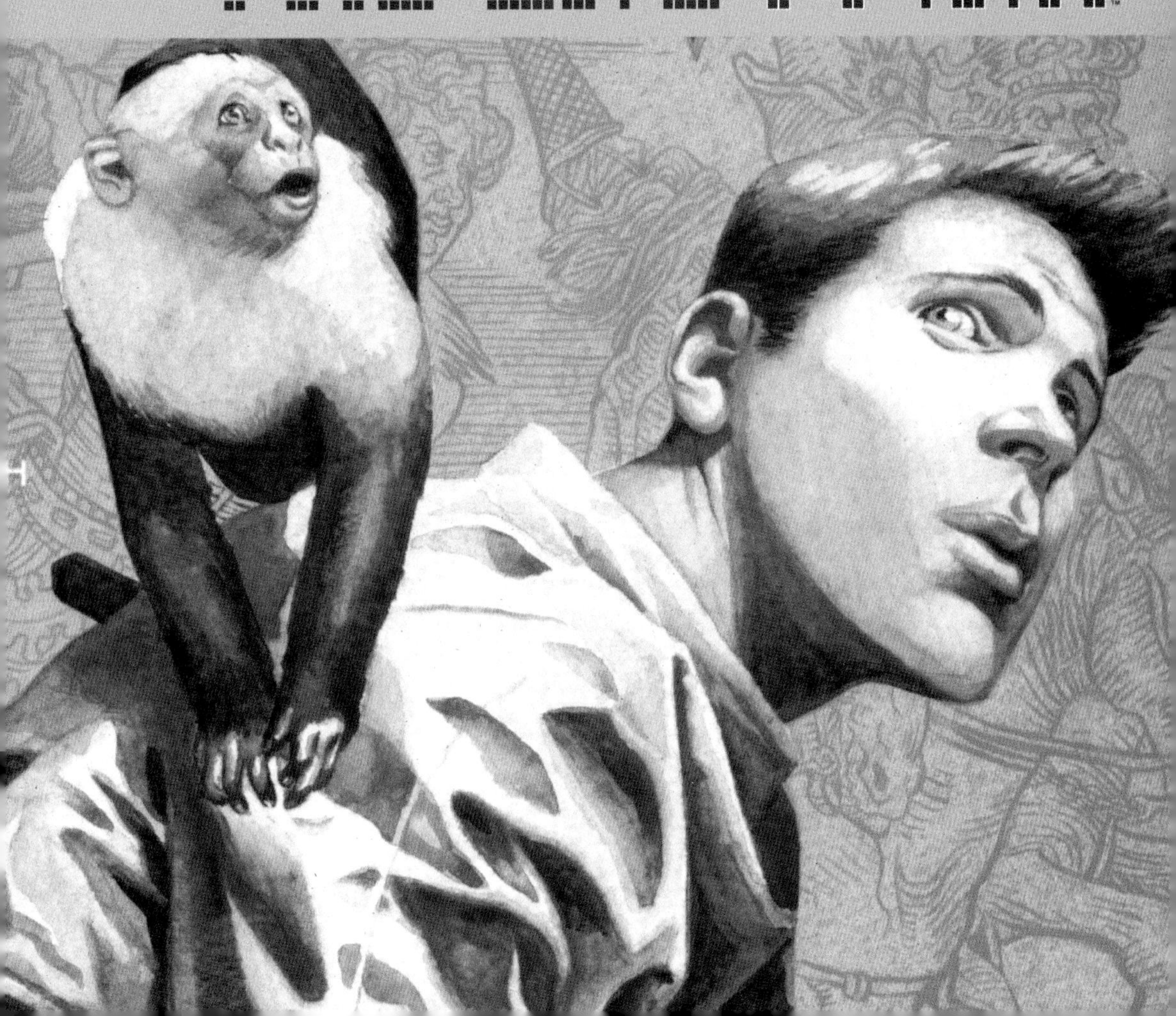

Y: THE LAST MAN VOL. 1: UNMANNED

Writer: Brian K. Vaughan | Artist: Pia Guerra
ISBN: 978-1-5638-9980-5 | Diamond Code: DEC108152 | Price: $14.99 | Format: TP
Collects issues #1-5.

Y: THE LAST MAN VOL. 2: CYCLES

Writer: Brian K. Vaughan | Artist: Pia Guerra
ISBN: 978-1-4012-0076-3 | Diamond Code: SEP128229 | Price: $14.99 | Format: TP
Collects issues #6-10.

Y: THE LAST MAN VOL. 3: ONE SMALL STEP

Writer: Brian K. Vaughan | Artist: Pia Guerra
ISBN: 978-1-4012-0201-9 | Diamond Code: FEB118093 | Price: $14.99 | Format: TP
Collects issues #11-17.

Y: THE LAST MAN VOL. 4: SAFEWORD

Writer: Brian K. Vaughan | Artist: Pia Guerra
ISBN: 978-1-4012-0232-3 | Diamond Code: DEC108199 | Price: $14.99 | Format: TP
Collects issues #18-23.

Y: THE LAST MAN VOL. 5: RING OF TRUTH

Writer: Brian K. Vaughan | Artist: Pia Guerra
ISBN: 978-1-4012-0487-7 | Diamond Code: MAY050306 | Price: $14.99 | Format: TP
Collects issues #24-31.

Y: THE LAST MAN VOL. 6: GIRL ON GIRL

Writer: Brian K. Vaughan | Artist: Pia Guerra
ISBN: 978-1-4012-0501-0 | Diamond Code: DEC108151 | Price: $14.99 | Format: TP
Collects issues #32-36.

Y: THE LAST MAN VOL. 7: PAPER DOLLS

Writer: Brian K. Vaughan | Artist: Pia Guerra
ISBN: 978-1-4012-1009-0 | Diamond Code: FEB060341 | Price: $14.99 | Format: TP
Collects issues #37-42.

Y: THE LAST MAN VOL. 8: KIMONO DRAGONS

Writer: Brian K. Vaughan | Artist: Pia Guerra
ISBN: 978-1-4012-1010-6 | Diamond Code: AUG060299 | Price: $14.99 | Format: TP
Collects issues #43-48.

Y: THE LAST MAN VOL. 9: MOTHERLAND

Writer: Brian K. Vaughan | Artist: Pia Guerra
ISBN: 978-1-4012-1351-0 | Diamond Code: FEB070362 | Price: $14.99 | Format: TP
Collects issues #49-54.

Y: THE LAST MAN VOL. 10: WHYS AND WHEREFORES

Writer: Brian K. Vaughan | Artist: Pia Guerra
ISBN: 978-1-4012-1813-3 | Diamond Code: MAR080241 | Price: $14.99 | Format: TP
Collects issues #55-60.

Defy expectation. Defy tradition. Defy skeptics, critics, and even the readers themselves. Vertigo has made and remade comics history with genre-defining titles such as THE SANDMAN, Y: THE LAST MAN, PREACHER, HELLBLAZER and FABLES. In 2014, with debut titles like COFFIN HILL, HINTERKIND, FBP: FEDERAL BUREAU OF PHYSICS, TRILLIUM, DEAD BOY DETECTIVES and THE WAKE, the entire line is brimming with jumping-on points for future classic collections. Be there as Vertigo defies convention and changes the conversation with the most cutting-edge graphic storytelling in the industry.

FBP: FEDERAL BUREAU OF PHYSICS VOL. 1: THE PARADIGM SHIFT

Writer: Simon Oliver | Artist: Robbi Rodriguez

ISBN: 978-1-4012-4510-8 | Diamond Code: NOV130274 | Price: $9.99 | Format: TP

It started small: temporary gravity failures, time reversal loops. Things are getting worse, and it falls to Adam Hardy and his Federal Bureau of Physics team to figure out what's going on.

100 BULLETS: BROTHER LONO

Writer: Brian Azzarello | Artist: Eduardo Risso

ISBN: 978-1-4012-4506-1 | Diamond Code: JAN140371 | Price: $16.99 | Format: TP

The Eisner Award-winning team behind 100 BULLETS—writer Brian Azzarello and artist Eduardo Risso—reunites to tell the story of the baddest Minuteman of all.

COFFIN HILL VOL. 1: FOREST OF NIGHT

Writer: Caitlin Kittredge | Artist: Inaki Miranda

ISBN: 978-1-4012-4887-1 | Diamond Code: FEB140285 | Price: $9.99 | Format: TP

Following a night of sex, drugs and witchcraft in the woods, Eve Coffin wakes up to find one friend is missing, one is in a mental ward, and no one knows that Eve is responsible.

HINTERKIND VOL. 1: THE WAKING WORLD

Writer: Ian Edginton | Artist: Francesco Trifolgi

ISBN: 978-1-4012-4518-4 | Diamond Code: JAN140379 | Price: $9.99 | Format: TP

In a post-apocalyptic world where humans have been pushed to the edge of extinction by the creatures of fantasy and fables, Prosper Monday is determined to put the world right again.

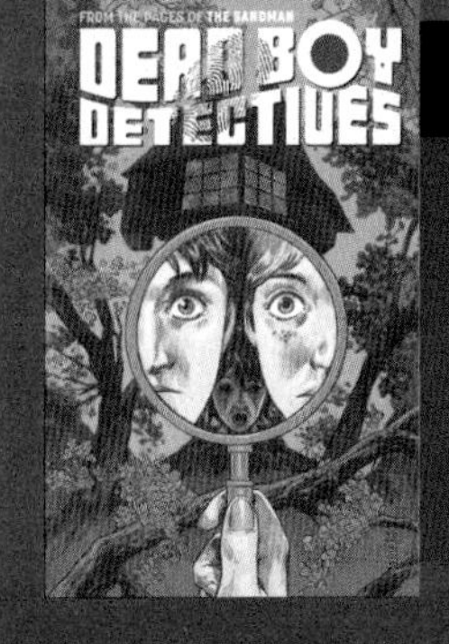

DEAD BOY DETECTIVES VOL. 1: SCHOOLBOY TERRORS

Writer: Toby Litt | Artist: Mark Buckingham

ISBN: 978-1-4012-4889-5 | Diamond Code: MAR140290 | Price: $9.99 | Format: TP

From the pages of THE SANDMAN, Neil Gaiman's intrepid dead schoolboys head back to the horror that is St. Hilarion's School—the place where they both were murdered.

ALAN MOORE

ALAN MOORE has crafted some of the most celebrated and cherished stories the comic book industry has ever seen, breaking new ground with titles such as **SAGA OF THE SWAMP THING** and the best-selling graphic novel of all time, **WATCHMEN**. His work on titles such as **THE LEAGUE OF EXTRAORDINARY GENTLEMEN**, **PROMETHEA** and **V FOR VENDETTA** has defined a generation of readers and helped usher in an era in which the graphic novel became a serious form of artistic expression.

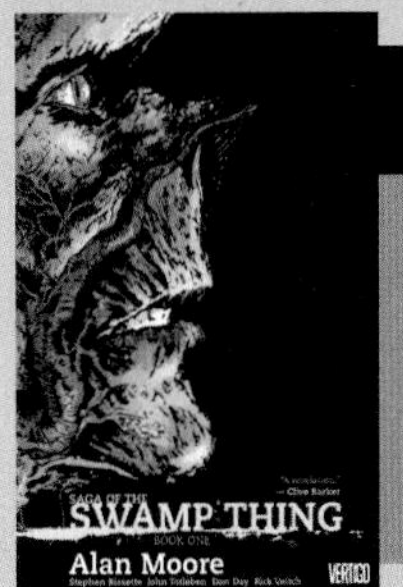

SAGA OF THE SWAMP THING BOOK ONE

Writer: Alan Moore | Artists: Stephen Bissette

ISBN: 978-1-4012-2083-9 | Diamond Code: JAN120343 | Price: $19.99 | Format: TP

Alan Moore's take on the classic monster that stretched the creative boundaries of the medium and became one of the most spectacular series in comic book history.

V FOR VENDETTA

Writer: Alan Moore | Artist: David Lloyd

ISBN: 978-1-4012-0841-7 | Diamond Code: SEP088030 | Price: $19.99 | Format: TP

Alan Moore's iconic tale set in a near-future dystopian London and its revolutionary hero "V."

PROMETHEA BOOK 1

Writer: Alan Moore | Artist: J.H. Williams III

ISBN: 978-1-5638-9667-5 | Diamond Code: APR108106 | Price: $17.99 | Format: TP

Alan Moore's psychedelic tale of Sophia, an ordinary college student who is transformed into Promethea, the living embodiment of imagination.

THE LEAGUE OF EXTRAORDINARY GENTLEMEN VOL. 1

Writer: Alan Moore | Artist: Kevin O'Neill

ISBN: 978-1-5638-9858-7 | Diamond Code: MAY118167 | Price: $16.99 | Format: TP

The best-known characters of 19th Century literature band together in Alan Moore's award-winning graphic novel.

THE LEAGUE OF EXTRAORDINARY GENTLEMEN VOL. 2

Writer: Alan Moore | Artist: Kevin O'Neill

ISBN: 978-1-4012-0118-0 | Diamond Code: MAY118168 | Price: $16.99 | Format: TP

The League must reassemble to combat an impending invasion.

THE LEAGUE OF EXTRAORDINARY GENTLEMEN: BLACK DOSSIER

Writer: Alan Moore | Artist: Kevin O'Neill

ISBN: 978-1-4012-0307-8 | Diamond Code: JUL080193 | Price: $19.99 | Format: TP

Disbanded and disavowed, the remaining members of the League search for the Black Dossier to save the country from an iron-fisted regime.

GRANT MORRISON has been working with Vertigo for twenty years, creating some of the most seminal works in the imprint's history, starting with ANIMAL MAN and DOOM PATROL. His reality-bending themes, provocative storytelling and otherwordly concepts have endeared him to mainstream culture at-large as one of the most groundbreaking minds in the medium.
GRANT MORRISON
BOLLAND

ANIMAL MAN VOL. 1

Writer: Grant Morrison | Artists: Chas Truog, Doug Hazlewood & Tom Grummet
ISBN: 978-1-5638-9005-5 | Diamond Code: OCT068037 | Price: $19.99 | Format: TP

The bizarre adventures of Animal Man, a second-rate superhero struggling with real-life issues and moral dilemmas.

DOOM PATROL VOL. 1: CRAWLING FROM THE WRECKAGE

Writer: Grant Morrison | Artists: Richard Case, Doug Braithwaite & others
ISBN: 978-1-5638-9034-5 | Diamond Code: JAN058100 | Price: $19.99 | Format: TP

Grant Morrison reinvents the strange superhero team.

FLEX MENTALLO: MAN OF MUSCLE MYSTERY

Writer: Grant Morrison | Artist: Frank Quitely
ISBN: 978-1-4012-4702-7 | Diamond Code: JAN140382 | Price: $14.99 | Format: TP

From the pages of DOOM PATROL, the award-winning team behind ALL-STAR SUPERMAN takeS on Flex Mentallo.

JOE THE BARBARIAN

Writer: Grant Morrison | Artist: Sean Murphy
ISBN: 978-1-4012-3747-9 | Diamond Code: DEC120365 | Price: $19.99 | Format: TP

Thirteen-year-old diabetic Joe Manson is transported to a fantasy land where he's the world's last hope.

THE INVISIBLES VOL. 1: SAY YOU WANT A REVOLUTION

Writer: Grant Morrison | Artists: Steve Yeowell & Jill Thompson
ISBN: 978-1-5638-9267-7 | Diamond Code: SEP068118 | Price: $19.99 | Format: TP

Throughout history, a secret society called the Invisibles has worked against dark forces conspiring to end mankind.

WE3

Writer: Grant Morrison | Artist: Frank Quitely
ISBN: 978-1-4012-4302-9 | Diamond Code: NOV130270 | Price: $14.99 | Format: TP

Grant Morrison and Frank Quitely deliver the emotional journey of three housepets who are weaponized for lethal combat by the government.

MAD

THE MAD ARCHIVES VOL. 1

By: The Usual Gang Of Idiots
ISBN: 978-1-4012-3786-8 | Diamond Code: APR120274 | Price: $59.99 | Format: HC

Collects the original *MAD* series issues #1-6.

THE MAD ARCHIVES VOL. 2

By: The Usual Gang Of Idiots
ISBN: 978-1-4012-3787-5 | Diamond Code: APR120275 | Price: $59.99 | Format: HC

Collects the original *MAD* series issues #7-12.

THE MAD ARCHIVES VOL. 3

By: The Usual Gang Of Idiots
ISBN: 978-1-4012-3427-0 | Diamond Code: SEP110209 | Price: $59.99 | Format: HC

Collects the original *MAD* series issues #13-18.

THE MAD ARCHIVES VOL. 4

By: The Usual Gang Of Idiots
ISBN: 978-1-4012-3761-5 | Diamond Code: APR120273 | Price: $59.99 | Format: HC

Collects the original *MAD* series issues #19-24.

EPIC MAD

By: The Usual Gang Of Idiots
ISBN: 978-1-4012-3762-2 | Diamond Code: DEC118177 | Price: $12.99 | Format: TP

Your favorite *MAD Magazine* parodies and segments available in one low-priced digest.

AMAZINGLY STUPID MAD

By: The Usual Gang Of Idiots
ISBN: 978-1-4012-3857-5 | Diamond Code: MAY120312 | Price: $12.99 | Format: TP

Ripped from the pages of *MAD Magazine*, the "finest" moments designed for fans of the Cartoon Network show!

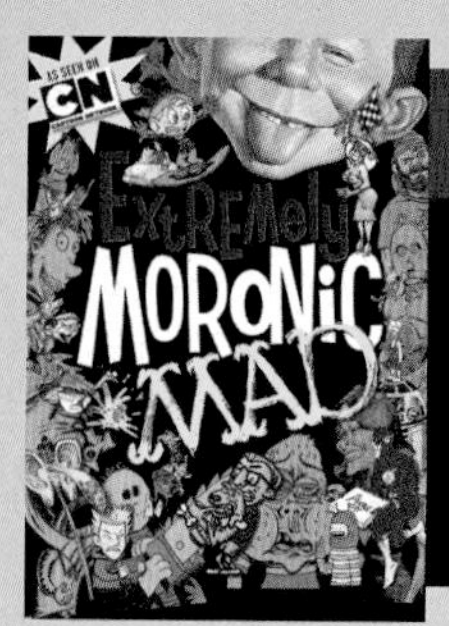

EXTREMELY MORONIC MAD

By: The Usual Gang Of Idiots

ISBN: 978-1-4012-3861-2 | Diamond Code: JUL120238 | Price: $12.99 | Format: TP

More ridiculous hilarity from MAD!

TOTALLY USELESS MAD

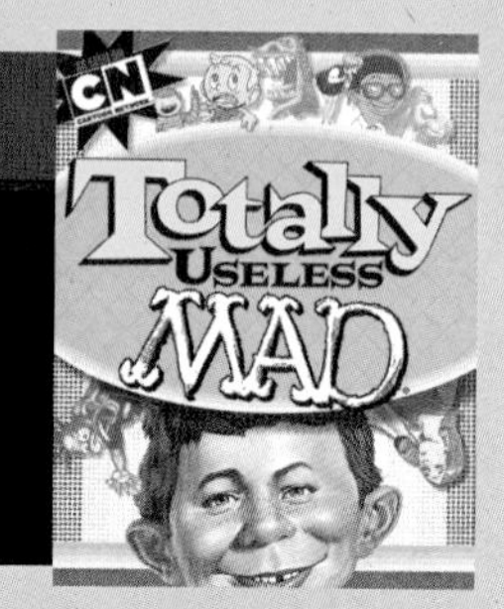

By: The Usual Gang Of Idiots

ISBN: 978-1-4012-3911-4| Diamond Code: JAN130326 | Price: $12.99 | Format: TP

Insane, awesome and insanely awesome "best-of" features from MAD!

DISTURBINGLY AWFUL MAD

By: The Usual Gang Of Idiots

ISBN: 978-1-4012-4190-2 | Diamond Code: MAY130245 | Price: $12.99 | Format: TP

Haven't got enough? Here's more of the best of the worst of MAD.

INTENSELY DUMB MAD

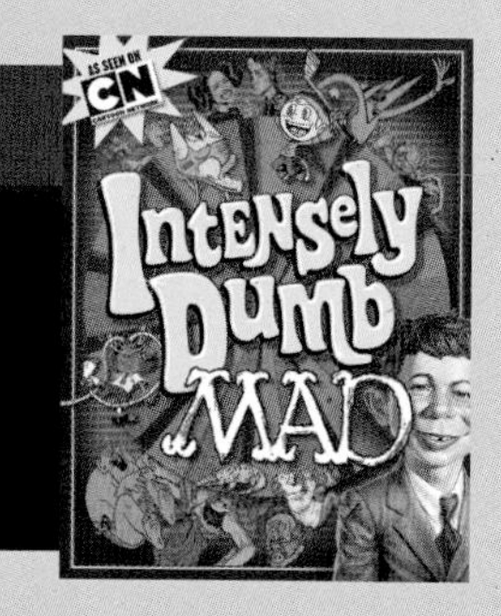

By: The Usual Gang Of Idiots

ISBN: 978-1-4012-4191-9 | Diamond Code: JUL130255 | Price: $12.99 | Format: TP

If you needed more MAD, look no further!

SPY VS. SPY: THE TOP SECRET FILES

By: Peter Kuper

ISBN: 978-1-4012-3527-7 | Diamond Code: AUG118124 | Price: $9.99 | Format: TP

The continuing adventures of the popular MAD Magazine serial by Peter Kuper.

SPY VS. SPY: FIGHT TO THE FINISH

By: Peter Kuper

ISBN: 978-1-4012-4814-7 | Diamond Code: AUG138237 | Price: $9.99 | Format: TP

The diabolical duo of double-crosses and deceit (one dressed in black, the other in white) continue to one-up each other until death do they part.

DC COMICS: All Ages

All-ages graphic novels ranging from the crime-fighting team-ups in THE ALL-NEW BATMAN: THE BRAVE AND THE BOLD to the heroics of SUPERMAN FAMILY ADVENTURES to the playground escapades of TINY TITANS!

TINY TITANS: WELCOME TO THE TREEHOUSE

Written and illustrated by Art Baltazar and Franco
ISBN: 978-1-4012-2078-5 | Diamond Code: NOV080197 | Price: $12.99 | Format: TP
Collects issues #1-6.

TINY TITANS: ADVENTURES IN AWESOMENESS

Written and illustrated by Art Baltazar and Franco
ISBN: 978-1-4012-2328-1 | Diamond Code: FEB090225 | Price: $12.99 | Format: TP
Collects issues #7-12.

TINY TITANS: SIDEKICKIN' IT

Written and illustrated by Art Baltazar and Franco
ISBN: 978-1-4012-2653-4 | Diamond Code: NOV090199 | Price: $12.99 | Format: TP
Collects issues #13-18.

TINY TITANS: THE FIRST RULE OF PET CLUB...

Written and illustrated by Art Baltazar and Franco
ISBN: 978-1-4012-2892-7 | Diamond Code: JUN100232 | Price: $12.99 | Format: TP
Collects issues #19-25.

TINY TITANS: FIELD TRIPPIN'

Written and illustrated by Art Baltazar and Franco
ISBN: 978-1-4012-3173-6 | Diamond Code: FEB110238 | Price: $12.99 | Format: TP
Collects issues #26-32.

TINY TITANS: THE TREEHOUSE AND BEYOND!

Written and illustrated by Art Baltazar & Franco
ISBN: 978-1-4012-3310-5 | Diamond Code: SEP110204 | Price: $12.99 | Format: TP

Collects issues #33-38.

TINY TITANS: GROWING UP TINY!

Writers: Art Baltazar & Franco | Artists: Art Baltazar and Franco
ISBN: 978-1-4012-3525-3 | Diamond Code: MAR120269 | Price: $12.99 | Format: TP

Collects issues #39-44.

SUPERMAN FAMILY ADVENTURES VOL. 1

Writers: Art Baltazar & Franco | Artists: Art Baltazar and Franco
ISBN: 978-1-4012-4050-9 | Diamond Code: MAR130290 | Price: $12.99 | Format: TP

Superman! Superboy! Supergirl! Krypto the Superdog! The entire Superman family is re-imagined here in this energetic all-ages graphic novel.

BATMAN: LI'L GOTHAM VOL. 1

Writers: Derek Fridolfs & Dustin Nguyen | Artist: Dustin Nguyen
ISBN: 978-1-4012-4494-1 | Diamond Code: NOV130255 | Price: $12.99 | Format: TP

Follow all of your favorite Gotham City characters throughout each holiday in these gorgeously drawn and painted all-ages tales!

THE ALL-NEW BATMAN: THE BRAVE AND THE BOLD VOL. 1

Writer: Sholly Fisch | Artist: Rick Burchett
ISBN: 978-1-4012-3272-6 | Diamond Code: JUN110329 | Price: $12.99 | Format: TP

Spinning out of the Cartoon Network series comes the further adventures of the Caped Crusader!

DC COMICS READING ORDER

BATMAN BACKLIST AND SUGGESTED READING ORDER

	ISBN/Diamond Code	Title	Author/Artist	US$/Format
1.	9781401231156/ MAY110240	Batman: Mad Love and Other Stories	Dini, Paul/Various	17.99/ TP
2.	9781401232948/ AUG110254	Tales of the Batman: Don Newton	Various/ Newton, Don	$39.99/ HC
3.	9781401231019/ MAR110346	Tales of the Batman: Gene Colan Vol. 1	Various/ Colan, Gene	$39.99/ HC
4.	9781401235376/ MAR120248	Batman: Illustrated by Neal Adams Vol. 1	Various/ Adams, Neal	$24.99/ TP
5.	9781401238360/ JAN130308	Batman: Illustrated by Neal Adams Vol. 2	Adams, Neal/ Adams, Neal	$24.99/ TP
6.	9781401240752/ APR130227	Batman Illustrated by Neal Adams Vol. 3	Adams, Neal/ Various	$24.99/ TP
7.	9781401236847/ JUL130240	Batman: Odyssey	Adams, Neal/ Adams, Neal	$19.99/ TP
8.	9781401238292/ MAR130280	Tales of the Batman: Archie Goodwin	Goodwin, Archie/ Various	$39.99/ HC
9.	9781401247645/ NOV130238	Batman by Doug Moench and Kelley Jones Vol. 1	Moench, Doug/ Jones, Kelley	$39.99/ HC
10.	9781401236816/ JUN120241	Legends of the Dark Knight: Alan Davis	Davis, Alan/ Davis, Alan	$39.99/ HC
11.	9781401242961/ MAY130233	Legends of the Dark Knight: Jim Aparo Vol. 2	Aparo, Jim/ Haney, Bob	$49.99/ HC
12.	9781401232276/ JUN110268	Legends of the Dark Knight: Marshall Rogers	Englehart, Steve/ Rogers, Marshall	$49.99/ HC
13.	9781401242398/ JUN130259	Batman: Legends of the Dark Knight Vol. 1	Various/ Various	$14.99/ TP
14.	9781401204457/ JAN050275	Batman Chronicles Vol. 1	Finger, Bill/ Kane, Bob	$14.99/ TP
15.	9781401207526/ OCT060163	Batman: Year One	Miller, Frank/ Mazzucchelli, David	$14.99/ TP
16.	9781401216269/ SEP080167	Batman: The Man Who Laughs	Brubaker, Ed/ Mahnke, Doug	$14.99/ TP
17.	9781563892738/ APR058324	Batman: Haunted Knight	Loeb, Jeph/ Sale, Tim	$14.99/ TP
18.	9781401232597/ JUL110251	Batman: The Long Halloween	Loeb, Jeph/ Sale, Tim	$24.99/ TP
19.	9781401244019/ NOV130237	Batman: Dark Victory	Loeb, Jeph/ Sale, Tim	$24.99/ TP
20.	9781401201876/ APR050327	Batman/Superman/ Wonder Woman: Trinity	Wagner, Matt/ Wagner, Matt	$17.99/ TP

DC COMICS READING ORDER

	ISBN/Diamond Code	Title	Author/Artist	US$/Format
21.	9781401235154/ FEB120260	Batman: Prey	Moench, Doug/ Gulacy, Paul	$24.99/ TP
22.	9781401232740/ JUN110267	Batman: A Death In the Family	Starlin, Jim/ Aparo, Jim	$24.99/ TP
23.	9781401215491/ JUN070170	Batman: Gothic	Morrison, Grant/ Janson, Klaus	$14.99/ TP
24.	9781401204259/ AUG050185	Batman: Arkham Asylum	Morrison, Grant/ McKean, Dave	$17.99/ TP
25.	9781401216672/ NOV070226	Batman: The Killing Joke	Moore, Alan/ Bolland, Brian	$17.99/ HC
26.	9781401233839/ JAN120305	Batman: Venom	O'Neil, Dennis J./ Garcia-Lopez, Jose Luis	$14.99/ TP
27.	9781401233792/ JAN120303	Batman: Knightfall Vol. 1	Various/ Various	$39.99/ TP
28.	9781401235369/ FEB120266	Batman: Knightfall Vol. 2	Various/ Various	$29.99/ TP
29.	9781401237219/ JUN120242	Batman: Knightfall Vol. 3	Various/ Various	$29.99/ TP
30.	9781401232283/ AUG110242	Batman: No Man's Land Vol.1	Various/ Various	$29.99/ TP
31.	9781401233808/ JAN120304	Batman: No Man's Land Vol. 2	Various/ Various	$29.99/ TP
32.	9781401234560/ MAY120289	Batman: No Man's Land Vol. 3	Various/ Various	$34.99/ TP
33.	9781401235642/ SEP120237	Batman: No Man's Land Vol. 4	Various/ Various	$34.99/ TP
34.	9781401223175/ MAY090178	Batman: Hush	Loeb, Jeph/ Lee, Jim	$24.99/ TP
35.	9781401242428/ OCT130247	Batman Unwrapped by Andy Kubert	Kubert, Andy/ Kubert, Andy	$34.99/ HC
36.	9781401238902/ JAN130307	Batman Noir: Eduardo Risso: The Deluxe Edition	Risso, Eduardo/ Azzarello, Brian	$24.99/ HC
37.	9781401231453/ MAY110241	Batman: Under The Red Hood	Winick, Judd/ Mahnke, Doug	$29.99/ TP
38.	9781401231644/ MAR110343	Batman: Red Hood: Lost Days	Winick, Judd/ Various	$14.99/ TP
39.	9781401244026/ OCT130238	Batman: Batman and Son	Morrison, Grant/Kubert, Andy/ Williams III, J.H.	$19.99/ TP
40.	9781401220327/ FEB090202	Batman: The Resurrection Ra's al Ghul	Various/ Various	$19.99/ TP
41.	9781401225766/ MAR100237	Batman: R.I.P.	Morrison, Grant/ Daniel, Tony S.	$14.99/ TP

DC COMICS READING ORDER

	ISBN/Diamond Code	Title	Author/Artist	US$/Format
42.	9781401222826/ MAR100239	Final Crisis	Morrison, Grant/ Jones, J.G.	$19.99/ TP
43.	9781401227241/ APR100218	Batman: Whatever Happened To The Caped Crusader?	Gaiman, Neil/ Kubert, Andy	$14.99/ TP
44.	9781401224172/ AUG100199	Batman: Battle for the Cowl	Daniel, Tony S./ Daniel, Tony S.	$14.99/ TP
45.	9781401221249/ DEC090202	Batman: Heart of Hush	Dini, Paul/ Nguyen, Dustin	$14.99/ TP
46.	9781401229061/ AUG110246	Batman: Streets of Gotham Vol. 2: Leviathan	Dini, Paul/ Nguyen, Dustin	$17.99/ TP
47.	9781401231309/ MAY120291	Batman: Streets of Gotham Vol. 3: House of Hush	Dini, Paul/ Nguyen, Dustin	$17.99/ TP
48.	9781401229870/ DEC100246	Batman & Robin Vol. 1: Batman Reborn	Morrison, Grant/ Quitely, Frank	$14.99/ TP
49.	9781401232719/ AUG110241	Batman & Robin Vol. 2: Batman vs. Robin	Morrison, Grant/ Stewart, Cameron	$17.99/ TP
50.	9781401235086/ FEB120258	Batman & Robin Vol. 3: Batman & Robin Must Die!	Morrison, Grant/ Frazer, Irving	$17.99/ TP
51.	9781401235390/ OCT120260	Batman & Robin: Dark Knight vs. White Knight	Various/ Various	$16.99/ TP
52.	9781401233822/ OCT110245	Batman: The Return of Bruce Wayne	Morrison, Grant/ Paquette, Yanick	$19.99/ TP
53.	9781401233471/ FEB120259	Batman: Bruce Wayne— The Road Home	Various/ Various	$17.99/ TP
54.	9781401229757/ JUL110250	Batman: Life After Death	Daniel, Tony S./ Daniel, Tony S.	$14.99/ TP
55.	9781401229900/ NOV110198	Batman: Time and the Batman	Various/ Various	$14.99/ TP
56.	9781401238278/ OCT120258	Batman, Incorporated	Morrison, Grant/ Paquette, Yanick	$19.99/ TP
57.	9781401242633/ AUG130293	Batman Incorporated Vol. 1: Demon Star (The New 52)	Morrison, Grant/ Burnham, Chris	$16.99/ TP
58.	9781401244002/ JUL130233	Batman Incorporated Vol. 2: Gotham's Most Wanted (The New 52)	Morrison, Grant/ Burnham, Chris	$24.99/ HC
59.	9781401230715/ MAR110340	Batman: Knight and Squire	Cornell, Paul/ Broxton, Jimmy	$14.99/ TP
60.	9781401234706/ JUL120220	Batman: Eye of the Beholder	Daniel, Tony S./ Daniel, Tony S.	$14.99/ TP
61.	9781401238285/ OCT120261	Batman: The Dark Knight: Golden Dawn	Finch, David/ Finch, David	$14.99/ TP
62.	9781401233419/ NOV110194	Batman: Gates of Gotham	Snyder, Scott/ McCarthy, Trevor	$14.99/ TP

DC COMICS READING ORDER

	ISBN/Diamond Code	Title	Author/Artist	US$/Format
63.	9781401232078/ NOV120268	Batman: The Black Mirror	Snyder, Scott/ Jock	$16.99/ TP
64.	9781401233389/ DEC110276	Flashpoint	Johns, Geoff/ Kubert, Andy	$14.99/ TP
65.	9781401234058/ DEC110277	Flashpoint: World of Flashpoint Featuring Batman	Azzarello, Brian/ Risso, Eduardo	$17.99/ TP
66.	9781401235420/ DEC120323	Batman Vol. 1: The Court of Owls (The New 52)	Snyder, Scott/ Capullo, Greg	$16.99/ TP
67.	9781401237783/ JUL130235	Batman Vol. 2: The City of Owls (The New 52)	Snyder, Scott/ Capullo, Greg Albuquerque, Rafael	$16.99/ TP
68.	9781401242527/ AUG130291	Batman: Night of the Owls (The New 52)	Snyder, Scott/ Capullo, Greg	$19.99/ TP
69.	9781401242343/ MAY130216	Batman Vol. 3: Death of the Family (The New 52)	Snyder, Scott/ Capullo, Greg	$24.99/ HC
70.	9781401245085/ JAN140342	Batman Vol. 4: Zero Year-Secret City (The New 52)	Snyder, Scott/ Capullo, Greg	$24.99/ HC
71.	9781401234676/ JAN130296	Batman: Detective Comics Vol. 1: Faces of Death (The New 52)	Daniel, Tony S./ Daniel, Tony S.	$16.99/ TP
72.	9781401242657/ AUG130290	Batman: Detective Comics Vol. 2: Scare Tactics (The New 52)	Daniel, Tony S./ Daniel, Tony S.; Benes, Ed	$16.99/ TP
73.	9781401242664/ JUL130232	Batman: Detective Comics Vol. 3: Emperor Penguin (The New 52)	Layman, John/ Fabok, Jason; Clarke, Andy	$24.99/ HC
74.	9781401237110/ APR130221	Batman: The Dark Knight Vol. 1: Knight Terrors (The New 52)	Jenkins, Paul; Finch, David/ Finch, David	$16.99/ TP
75.	9781401242824/ OCT130236	Batman: The Dark Knight Vol. 2: Cycle of Violence (The New 52)	Hurwitz, Gregg/ Finch, David	$14.99/ TP
76.	9781401242473/ SEP130269	Batman: The Dark Knight Vol. 3: Mad (The New 52)	Hurwitz, Gregg	$24.99/ HC
77.	9781401238384/ MAR130270	Batman & Robin Vol. 1: Born To Kill (The New 52)	Tomasi, Peter J./ Gleason, Patrick	$16.99/ TP
78.	9781401242671/ FEB130207	Batman & Robin Vol. 2: Pearl (The New 52)	Tomasi, Peter J./ Gleason, Patrick	$16.99/ TP
79.	9781401242688/ JUL130234	Batman & Robin Vol. 3: Death of the Family (The New 52)	Tomasi, Peter J./ Gleason, Patrick	$22.99/ HC
80.	9781401245092/ DEC130296	Batman/Superman Vol. 1: Cross World (The New 52)	Pak, Greg/ Lee, Jae	$22.99/ HC
81.	9781401220082/ MAR090174	All-Star Batman & Robin, The Boy Wonder Vol. 1	Miller, Frank/ Lee, Jim	$19.99/ TP
82.	9781401215897/ JUN070171	Batman: Black & White Vol. 1	Various/ Various	$19.99/ TP
83.	9781563899171/ JUN080234	Batman: Black & White Vol. 2	Various/ Various	$19.99/ TP

DC COMICS READING ORDER

	ISBN/Diamond Code	Title	Author/Artist	US$/Format
84.	9781401213541/ JUN080235	Batman: Black & White Vol. 3	Various/ Various	$19.99/ TP
85.	9781401215811/ JUL080124	Joker	Azzarello, Brian/ Bermejo, Lee	$19.99/ HC
86.	9781401245047/ APR130219	Absolute Joker/Luthor	Azzarello, Brian/ Bermejo, Lee	$99.99/ HC
87.	9781563893421/ NOV118095	Batman: The Dark Knight Returns	Miller, Frank/ Miller, Frank	$14.99/ TP
88.	9781563899294/ FEB058404	Batman: The Dark Knight Strikes Again	Miller, Frank/ Miller, Frank	$19.99/ TP
89.	9781401247218/ DEC130307	Batman '66 Vol. 1	Parker, Jeff/ Various	$19.99/ HC
90.	9781401244958/ OCT130248	Batman: The TV Stories	Various/ Various	$14.99/ TP
91.	9781401234935/ JUN120243	Batman: Arkham City	Dini, Paul/ D'Anda, Carlos	$16.99/ TP
92.	9781401240189/ MAY130229	Batman: Arkham Unhinged Vol. 1	Dini, Paul; Fridolfs, Derek/ Various	$14.99/ TP
93.	9781401242831/ OCT130249	Batman: Arkham Unhinged Vol. 2	Fridolfs, Derek/ Various	$14.99/ TP
94.	9781401243050/ AUG130303	Batman: Arkham Unhinged Vol. 3	Fridolfs, Derek; Alexander, Jason Shawn/Various	$24.99/ HC
95.	9781401224196/ JUN100204	Batman: Cacophony	Smith, Kevin/ Flanagan, Walt	$14.99/ TP
96.	9781401228767/ JUN110270	Batman: The Widening Gyre	Smith, Kevin/ Flanagan, Walt	$17.99/ TP
97.	9781401233815/ DEC110282	Batman: Birth of the Demon	Barr, Mike W./ Various	$29.99/ TP
98.	9781401246426/ MAR140252	Damian: Son of Batman Deluxe Edition	Kubert, Andy/ Kubert, Andy	$24.99/ HC
99.	9781401237721/ OCT120259	Batman/Deathblow: After The Fire Deluxe Edition	Azzarello, Brian/ Bermejo, Lee	$22.99/ HC
100.	9781401237899/ FEB130217	Batman: Death by Design	Kidd, Chip/ Taylor, Dave	$14.99/ TP
101.	9781401232085/ MAR120234	Batman: Earth One	Johns, Geoff/ Frank, Gary	$22.99/ HC
102.	9781401211530/ DEC120332	Batman: Gotham by Gaslight	Augustyn, Brian/ Mignola, Mike	$12.99/ TP
103.	9781401236786/ SEP130278	The Batman/Judge Dredd Collection	Grant, Alan/ Wagner, John	$19.99/ TP
104.	9781401232139/ JUL110245	Batman: Noel	Bermejo, Lee/ Bermejo, Lee	$22.99/ HC

DC COMICS READING ORDER

	ISBN/Diamond Code	Title	Author/Artist	US$/Format
105.	9781401231842/ FEB110210	Planetary/Batman	Ellis, Warren/ Cassaday, John	$22.99/ HC
106.	9781401227876/ OCT120262	Batman: Through the Looking Glass	Jones, Bruce/ Kieth, Sam	$14.99/ TP
107.	9781401211929/ JAN130309	Batman: Year One Hundred	Pope, Paul/ Pope, Paul	$19.99/ TP

SUPERMAN BACKLIST AND SUGGESTED READING ORDER

	ISBN/Diamond Code	Title	Author/Artist	US$/Format
1.	9781401241896/ FEB130227	Superman: The Golden Age Omnibus Vol. 1	Siegel, Jerry/Shuster, Joe	$75.00/ HC
2.	9781401203399/ NOV058069	Superman: The Greatest Stories Ever Told	Various/ Various	$19.99/ TP
3.	9781401247041/ JUL130224	Superman: A Celebration of 75 Years	Various/ Various	$39.99 HC
4.	9781401247034/ JUL130225	Lois Lane: A Celebration of 75 Years	Various/ Various	$39.99/ HC
5.	9781401207649/ OCT138013	Superman Chronicles Vol. 1	Siegel, Jerry/ Shuster, Joe	$17.99/ TP
6.	9781401238377/ DEC120338	Showcase Presents: Superman Family Vol. 4	Various/ Various	$19.99/ TP
7.	9781401240486/ APR130229	Showcase Presents: DC Comics Presents - Superman Team-Ups Vol. 2	Various/ Various	$19.99/ TP
8.	9781401238568/ NOV120277	Adventures Of Superman: Jose Luis Garcia-Lopez	Garcia-Lopez, Jose-Luis/ Various	$39.99/ HC
9.	9781401204563/ FEB050263	Superman vs. The Flash	Various/ Various	$19.99/ TP
10.	9781401219406/ JUL080169	Superman vs. Brainiac	Various/ Various	$19.99/ TP
11.	9781401242565/ SEP130285	Superman vs. Mongul	Various/ Various	$14.99/ TP
12.	9781401238216/ NOV120273	Superman vs. Shazam!	Thomas, Roy/ Buckler, Rich; Kane, Gil	$19.99/ TP
13.	9781401238490/ DEC120339	Superman vs. Zod	Various/ Various	$9.99/ TP
14.	9781401240516/ APR130230	Superman: Phantom Zone	Gerber, Steve/ Colan, Gene	$14.99/ TP
15.	9781401243067/ JUL130247	Superman: Dark Knight Over Metropolis	Various/ Various	$14.99/ TP
16.	9781401227319/ APR100219	Superman: Whatever Happened to the Man of Tomorrow?	Moore, Alan/ Swan, Curt	$14.99/ TP
17.	9780930289287/ JUL058226	Superman: Man of Steel Vol. 1	Byrne, John/ Byrne, John	$14.99/ TP

DC COMICS READING ORDER

	ISBN/Diamond Code	Title	Author/Artist	US$/Format
18.	9781401200053/ MAR068126	Superman: Man of Steel Vol. 2	Byrne, John/ Byrne, John	$19.99/ TP
19.	9781401202460/ JUL088086	Superman: Man of Steel Vol. 3	Byrne, John/ Byrne, John	$19.99/ TP
20.	9781401204556/ JUN050349	Superman: Man of Steel Vol. 4	Byrne, John/ Byrne, John	$19.99/ TP
21.	9781401216795/ DEC070254	Superman: Man of Steel Vol. 6	Byrne, John/ Byrne, John	$19.99/ TP
22.	9781401238209/ OCT120268	Superman: The Man of Steel Vol. 7	Byrne, John/ Byrne, John; Ordway, Jerry	$19.99/ TP
23.	9781401243913/ OCT130252	Superman: The Man of Steel Vol. 8	Byrne, John/ Byrne, John	$16.99/ TP
24.	9781563895296/ FEB068194	Superman: For All Seasons	Loeb, Jeph/ Sale, Tim	$17.99/ TP
25.	9781401236885/ DEC120340	Superman: Reign of Doomsday	Cornell, Paul/ Rocafort, Kenneth	$16.99/ TP
26.	9781401241827/ OCT120269	Death of Superman	Jurgens, Dan/ Ordway, Jerry; Simonson, Louise; Bogdanove, Jon; Grummett, Tom	$14.99/ TP
27.	9781563891182/ MAY108143	A World Without Superman	Various/ Various	$19.99/ TP
28.	9781563891496/ OCT058018	The Return of Superman	Various/ Various	$19.99/ TP
29.	9781401238643/ NOV120276	Superman: The Death and Return of Superman Omnibus	Various/ Various	$99.99/ HC
30.	9781401229306/ JUN100212	Luthor	Azzarello, Brian/ Bermejo, Lee	$19.99/ TP
31.	9781401237806/ NOV120270	Superman: For Tomorrow	Azzarello, Brian/ Lee, Jim	$24.99/ TP
32.	9781401212056/ MAR080188	Superman: Camelot Falls Vol.1	Busiek, Kurt/ Pacheco, Carlos	$12.99/ TP
33.	9781401218652/ NOV080181	Superman: Camelot Falls Vol.2	Busiek, Kurt/ Pacheco, Carlos	$12.99/ TP
34.	9781401221324/ JAN100308	Superman: Coming of Atlas	Robinson, James/ Guedes, Renato	$14.99/ TP
35.	9781401232993/ SEP110188	Superman: Secret Origin	Johns, Geoff/ Frank, Gary	$19.99/ TP
36.	9781401237790/ OCT120270	Superman: Last Son of Krypton	Johns, Geoff; Donner, Richard/ Kubert, Adam; Frank, Gary	$19.99/ TP
37.	9781401220334/ FEB090217	Superman: Escape from Bizarro World	Johns, Geoff/ Powell, Eric	$14.99/ TP
38.	9781401219048/ APR090217	Superman And the Legion of Super-Heroes	Johns, Geoff/ Frank, Gary	$14.99/ TP

DC COMICS READING ORDER

	ISBN/Diamond Code	Title	Author/Artist	US$/Format
39.	9781401209544/ JUN060169	Superman: Up, Up & Away	Johns, Geoff/ Woods, Pete	$14.99/ TP
40.	9781401230760/ FEB120265	Superman: Grounded Vol. 1	Straczynski, Michael J./ Barrows, Eddy	$17.99/ TP
41.	9781401235321/ SEP120241	Superman: Grounded Vol. 2	Straczynski, J. Michael/ Barrows, Eddy	$14.99/ TP
42.	9781401230340/ NOV110203	Superman: The Black Ring Vol. 1	Cornel, Paul/ Woods, Pete	$14.99/ TP
43.	9781401234447/ JUN120255	Superman: The Black Ring Vol. 2	Cornell, Paul/ Woods, Pete	$16.99/ TP
44.	9781401232535/ AUG110260	Superman: Return of Doomsday	Various/ Various	$14.99/ TP
45.	9781401236885/ DEC120340	Superman: Reign of Doomsday	Cornell, Paul/ Rocafort, Kenneth	$16.99/ TP
46.	9781401246884/ JAN140346	Adventures of Superman Vol. 1	Various/ Various	$14.99/ TP
47.	9781401235475/ FEB130215	Superman: Action Comics Vol. 1: Superman and the Men of Steel (The New 52)	Morrison, Grant/ Morales, Rags	$16.99/ TP
48.	9781401242541/ SEP130275	Superman: Action Comics Vol. 2: Bulletproof (The New 52)	Morrison, Grant/ Morales, Rags	$16.99/ TP
49.	9781401242329/ AUG130298	Superman: Action Comics Vol. 3: at The End of Days (The New 52)	Morrison, Grant/ Morales, Rags	$24.99/ HC
50.	9781401236861/ MAR130274	Superman Vol. 1: What Price Tomorrow? (The New 52)	Pérez, George/ Meriño, Jesus; Scott, Nicola	$14.99/ TP
51.	9781401240288/ FEB130212	Superman Vol. 2: Secrets & Lies (The New 52)	Jurgens, Dan/ Giffen, Keith; Jurgens, Dan	$16.99/ TP
52.	9781401243203/ SEP130276	Superman Vol. 3: Fury At World's End (The New 52)	Lobdell, Scott/ Rocafort, Kenneth	$22.99/ HC
53.	9781401243197/ JUL130231	Superman: H'El On Earth (The New 52)	Lobdell, Scott/ Various	$29.99/ HC
54.	9781401201876/ APR050327	Batman/Superman/Wonder Woman:Trinity	Wagner, Matt/ Wagner, Matt	$17.99/ TP
55.	9781401240967/ FEB130216	Absolute Superman/Batman Vol. 1	Loeb, Jeph/McGuinness, Ed; Turner, Michael	$99.99/ HC
56.	9781401202200/ JUL090239	Superman/Batman: Public Enemies Vol. 1	Loeb, Jeph/ McGuinness, Ed	$14.99/ TP
57.	9781401202507/ SEP098202	Superman/Batman: Supergirl Vol. 2	Loeb, Jeph/ Turner, Michael	$14.99/ TP
58.	9781401207144/ AUG060184	Superman/Batman: Absolute Power Vol. 3	Loeb, Jeph/ Pacheco, Carlos	$12.99/ TP
59.	9781401210434/ AUG080185	Superman/Batman: Vengeance Vol. 4	Loeb, Jeph/ McGuinness, Ed	$12.99/ TP

DC COMICS READING ORDER

	ISBN/Diamond Code	Title	Author/Artist	US$/Format
60.	9781401217402/ NOV100234	Superman/Batman: Torment	Burnett, Alan/ Nguyen, Dustin	$14.99/ TP
61.	9781401228088/ MAY110252	Superman/Batman: Night & Day	Green, Michael/ Kolins, Scott	$17.99/ TP
62.	9781401229146/ SEP100256	Superman/Batman: Big Noise	Casey, Joe/ Kolins, Scott	$14.99/ TP
63.	9781401230326/ JAN110333	Superman/Batman: Worship	Levitz, Paul/ Guedes, Renato	$17.99/ TP
64.	9781401234461/ JUL120227	Superman/Batman: Sorcerer Kings	Bunn, Cullen/ Chriscross	$14.99/ TP
65.	9781401245092/ DEC130296	Batman/Superman Vol. 1: Cross World (The New 52)	Pak, Greg/ Lee, Jae	$22.99/ HC
66.	9781401222772/ MAR090192	Trinity Vol. 1	Busiek, Kurt/ Bagley, Mark	$29.99/ TP
67.	9781401223182/ MAY090196	Trinity Vol. 2	Busiek, Kurt/ Bagley, Mark	$29.99/ TP
68.	9781401223571/ JUL090243	Trinity Vol. 3	Busiek, Kurt/ Bagley, Mark	$29.99/ TP
69.	9781401224691/ FEB130226	Superman: Earth One	Straczynski, J. Michael/ Davis, Shane	$12.99/ TP
70.	9781401235598/ DEC130312	Superman: Earth One Vol. 2	Straczynski, J. Michael/ Davis, Shane	$14.99/ TP
71.	9781401204518/ JAN130315	Superman: Secret Identity	Busiek, Kurt/ Immonen, Stuart	$19.99/ TP
72.	9781401202521/ JUL050214	Superman: Birthright	Waid, Mark/ Immonen, Stuart	$19.99/ TP
73.	9781401232054/ JUL110247	All-Star Superman	Morrison, Grant/ Quitely, Frank	$29.99/ TP
74.	9781401228415/ APR100224	Superman vs. Muhammad Ali Deluxe Edition	O'Neil, Dennis/ Adams, Neil	$19.99/ HC
75.	9781401201913/ NOV058130	Superman: Red Son	Millar, Mark/ Johnson, Dave	$17.99/ TP
76.	9781563899584/ Star17970	Bizarro Comics	Various/ Various	$19.95/ TP

GREEN LANTERN BACKLIST AND SUGGESTED READING ORDER

	ISBN/Diamond Code	Title	Author/Artist	US$/Format
1.	9781401209612/ MAY060165	Green Lantern: The Greatest Stories Ever Told	Various/ Various	$19.99/ TP
2.	9781401219864/ JUL080158	Green Lantern: In Brightest Day	Broome, John/ Kane, Gil	$19.99/ TP
3.	9781401221638/ JAN090229	Green Lantern Chronicles Vol. 1	Broome, John/ Kane, Gil	$14.99/ TP

DC COMICS READING ORDER

	ISBN/Diamond Code	Title	Author/Artist	US$/Format
4.	9781401224998/ SEP090166	Green Lantern Chronicles Vol. 2	Broome, John/ Kane, Gil	$14.99/ TP
5.	9781401229153/ JUL100197	Green Lantern Chronicles Vol. 3	Broome, John/ Kane, Gil	$14.99/ TP
6.	9781401233969/ DEC110295	Green Lantern Chronicles Vol. 4	Broome, John/ Kane, Gil	$14.99/ TP
7.	9781401235178/ MAY120290	Green Lantern/Green Arrow	O'Neil, Dennis/ Adams, Neal	$29.99/ TP
8.	9781401236892/ AUG120252	Green Lantern: Sector 2814 Vol. 1	Wein, Len/ Gibbons, Dave	$16.99/ TP
9.	9781401240783/ MAY130231	Green Lantern: Sector 2814 Vol. 2	Wein, Len/ Gibbons, Dave	$16.99/ TP
10.	9781401243272/ OCT130250	Green Lantern: Sector 2814 Vol. 3	Englehart, Steve/Staton, Joe; Patterson, Bruce D.	$16.99/ TP
11.	9781401227555/ FEB100185	Green Lantern: Rebirth	Johns, Geoff/ Van Sciver, Ethan	$14.99/ TP
12.	9781401210588/ FEB080244	Green Lantern: No Fear	Johns, Geoff/ Pacheco, Carlos	$12.99/ TP
13.	9781401209605/ JUN098401	Green Lantern: Revenge of the Green Lanterns	Johns, Geoff/ Pacheco, Carlos	$14.99/ TP
14.	9781401215903/ OCT080170	Green Lantern: Wanted: Hal Jordan	Johns, Geoff/ Reis, Ivan	$29.99/ TP
15.	9781401233013/ JUN110275	Green Lantern: The Sinestro Corps War	Johns, Geoff/ Reis, Ivan	$29.99/ TP
16.	9781401223267/ MAR090178	Green Lanterns: Tales of the Sinestro Corps	Various/ Various	$14.99/ TP
17.	9781401230869/ JAN110337	Green Lantern: Secret Origin	Johns, Geoff/ Reis, Ivan	$14.99/ TP
18.	9781401223021/ APR100214	Green Lantern: Rage of the Red Lanterns	Johns, Geoff/ Reis, Ivan	$14.99/ TP
19.	9781401224202/ AUG100204	Green Lantern: Agent Orange	Johns, Geoff/ Tan, Philip	$14.99/ TP
20.	9781401228064/ APR110195	Blackest Night: Rise of the Black Lanterns	Various/ Various	$19.99/ TP
21.	9781401228071/ APR110196	Blackest Night: Tales of the Corps	Various/ Various	$19.99/ TP
22.	9781401229535/ APR110192	Blackest Night	Johns, Geoff/ Reis, Ivan	$19.99/ TP
23.	9781401229528/ APR110193	Blackest Night: Green Lantern	Johns, Geoff/ Mahnke, Doug	$19.99/ TP
24.	9781401228057/ APR110194	Blackest Night: Green Lantern Corps	Tomasi, Peter J./ Gleason, Patrick	$19.99/ TP

DC COMICS READING ORDER

	ISBN/Diamond Code	Title	Author/Artist	US$/Format
25.	9781401228040/ APR110197	Blackest Night: Black Lantern Corps Vol. 1	Various/ Various	$19.99/ TP
26.	9781401228033/ APR110198	Blackest Night: Black Lantern Corps Vol. 2	Various/ Various	$19.99/ TP
27.	9781401240738/ JAN130306	Absolute Blackest Night	Johns, Geoff/ Reis, Ivan	$125.00/ HC
28.	9781401232764/ SEP110177	Brightest Day Vol. 1	Johns, Geoff/ Reis, Ivan	$19.99/ TP
29.	9781401230845/ FEB120255	Brightest Day Vol. 2	Johns, Geoff/ Reis, Ivan	$19.99/ TP
30.	9781401232177/ JUN120244	Brightest Day Vol. 3	Johns, Geoff/ Reis, Ivan	$16.99/ TP
31.	9781401231415/ FEB120254	Green Lantern: Brightest Day	Johns, Geoff/ Mahnke, Doug	$19.99/ TP
32.	9781401234522/ JUN120246	Green Lantern: War of the Green Lanterns	Various/ Various	$16.99/ TP
33.	9781401235383/ OCT120265	War of the Green Lanterns: Aftermath	Tomasi, Peter J.; Bedard, Tony/Various	$16.99/ TP
34.	9781401234065/ DEC110280	Flashpoint: The World Of Flash-point Featuring Green Lantern	Various/ Various	$17.99/ TP
35.	9781401234553/ JAN120301	Green Lantern Vol. 1: Sinestro (The New 52)	Johns, Geoff/ Mahnke, Doug	$14.99/ TP
36.	9781401237677/ JUL130229	Green Lantern Vol. 2: The Revenge Of Black Hand (The New 52)	Johns, Geoff/Mahnke, Doug; Van Sciver, Ethan	$16.99/ TP
37.	9781401246846/ JAN140338	Green Lantern Vol. 3: The End (The New 52)	Johns, Geoff/ Mahnke, Doug	$19.99/ TP
38.	9781401246136/ DEC130302	Green Lantern: Rise of the Third Army (The New 52)	Johns, Geoff; Tomasi, Peter J./Various	$24.99/ TP
39.	9781401244095/ OCT130240	Green Lantern: Wrath of the First Lantern (The New 52)	Johns, Geoff/ Various	$29.99/ HC
40.	9781401247447/ DEC130303	Green Lantern Vol. 4: Dark Days (The New 52)	Venditti, Robert/ Tan, Billy	$24.99/ HC
41.	9781401248161/ FEB140249	Green Lantern: Lights Out (The New 52)	Venditti, Robert; Jensen, Van; Jordan, Justin; Soule, Charles/Tan, Billy; Chang, Bernard; Vitti, Allesandro; Walker, Brad	$24.99/ HC
42.	9781401221553/ NOV080187	Tales Of Green Lantern Corps Vol. 1	Various/ Various	$19.99/ TP
43.	9781401227029/ OCT090254	Tales Of Green Lantern Corps Vol. 2	Various/ Various	$19.99/ TP
44.	9781401229344/ SEP100259	Tales Of Green Lantern Corps Vol. 3	Various/ Various	$19.99/ TP
45.	9781401213565/ AUG098053	Green Lantern Corps: To Be a Lantern	Gibbons, Dave/ Gleason, Patrick	$14.99/ TP

DC COMICS READING ORDER

	ISBN/Diamond Code	Title	Author/Artist	US$/Format
46.	9781401222734/ MAR090182	Green Lantern Corps: Sins of the Star Sapphire	Tomasi, Peter J./ Gleason, Patrick	$14.99/ TP
47.	9781401219758/ AUG080181	Green Lantern Corps: Ring Quest	Tomasi, Peter J./ Gleason, Patrick	$14.99/ TP
48.	9781401225292/ AUG100205	Green Lantern Corps: Emerald Eclipse	Tomasi, Peter J./ Gleason, Patrick	$14.99/ TP
49.	9781401231408/ MAR120252	Green Lantern Corps: Revolt of the Alpha Lanterns	Bedard, Tony/ Syaf, Ardian	$14.99/ TP
50.	9781401230807/ APR120252	Green Lantern: Emerald Warriors Vol. 1	Tomasi, Peter J./ Pasarin, Fernando	$14.99/ TP
51.	9781401234416/ JUL120222	Green Lantern Corps: The Weaponer	Bedard, Tony/ Kirkham, Tyler	$14.99/ TP
52.	9781401237028/ APR130218	Green Lantern Corps Vol. 1: Fearsome (The New 52)	Tomasi, Peter J./ Pasarin, Fernando	$16.99/ TP
53.	9781401242947/ SEP130267	Green Lantern Corps Vol. 2: Alpha War (The New 52)	Tomasi, Peter J./ Pasarin, Fernando	$14.99/ TP
54.	9781401244071/ AUG130294	Green Lantern Corps Vol. 3: Willpower (The New 52)	Tomasi, Peter J./ Pasarin, Fernando	$24.99/ HC
55.	9781401237080/ APR130216	Green Lantern: New Guardians Vol. 1: The Ring Bearer (The New 52)	Bedard, Tony/ Kirkman, Tyler	$14.99/ TP
56.	9781401242930/ OCT130239	Green Lantern: New Guardians Vol. 2: Beyond Hope (The New 52)	Bedard, Tony/ Kirkham, Tyler	$14.99/ TP
57.	9781401244064/ SEP130268	Green Lantern: New Guardians Vol. 3: Love & Death (The New 52)	Bedard, Tony/ Kuder, Aaron	$24.99/ HC
58.	9781401234911/ MAR120243	Red Lanterns Vol. 1: Blood and Rage (The New 52)	Milligan, Peter/ Benes, Ed	$14.99/ TP
59.	9781401238476/ DEC120329	Red Lanterns Vol. 2: The Death of the Red Lanterns (The New 52)	Milligan, Peter/Sepulveda, Miguel; Benes, Ed	$16.99/ TP
60.	9781401244149/ AUG130296	Red Lanterns Vol. 3: The Second Prophecy (The New 52)	Milligan, Peter/ Sepulveda, Miguel	$19.99/ TP

THE FLASH BACKLIST AND SUGGESTED READING ORDER

	ISBN/Diamond Code	Title	Author/Artist	US$/Format
1.	9781401224974/ AUG090173	Flash vs The Rogues	Broome, John/ Infantino, Carmine	$14.99/ TP
2.	978-1401224714/ OCT138012	The Flash Chronicles Vol. 1	Various/ Infantino, Carmine	$17.99/ TP
3.	9781401238315/ JAN130310	The Flash Chronicles Vol. 4	Broome, John/ Infantino, Carmine	$14.99/ TP
4.	9781401230685/ JAN110328	The Flash Omnibus by Geoff Johns Vol. 1	Johns, Geoff/ Various	$75.00/ HC
5.	9781401233914/ NOV110197	The Flash Omnibus by Geoff Johns Vol. 2	Johns, Geoff/ Various	$75.00/ HC

DC COMICS READING ORDER

	ISBN/Diamond Code	Title	Author/Artist	US$/Format
6.	9781401237172/ APR120254	The Flash Omnibus by Geoff Johns Vol. 3	Johns, Geoff/ Various	$75.00/ HC
7.	9781401223342/ APR100213	Final Crisis: Rogue's Revenge	Johns, Geoff/ Kolins, Scott	$14.99/ TP
8.	9781401230012/ JAN110329	The Flash: Rebirth	Johns, Geoff/ Van Sciver, Ethan	$14.99/ TP
9.	9781401229702/ OCT100267	The Flash Vol. 1: Dastardly Death of the Rogues!	Johns, Geoff/ Manapul, Francis	$19.99/ TP
10.	9781401233389/ DEC110276	Flashpoint	Johns, Geoff/ Kubert, Andy	$14.99/ TP
11.	9781401234058/ DEC110277	Flashpoint: World of Flashpoint Featuring Batman	Various/ Various	$17.99/ TP
12.	9781401234065/ DEC110280	Flashpoint: World of Flashpoint Featuring Green Lantern	Various/ Various	$17.99/ TP
13.	9781401234102/ DEC110279	Flashpoint: World of Flashpoint Featuring Wonder Woman	Various/ Various	$17.99/ TP
14.	9781401234089/ DEC110281	Flashpoint: World of Flashpoint Featuring The Flash	Various/ Various	$17.99/ TP
15.	9781401234348/ DEC110278	Flashpoint: World of Flashpoint Featuring Superman	Various/ Various	$17.99/ TP
16.	9781401235543/ MAY130224	The Flash Vol. 1: Move Forward (The New 52)	Manapul, Francis; Buccellato, Brian/Manapul, Francis	$16.99/ TP
17.	9781401242732/ NOV130229	The Flash Vol. 2: Rogues Revolution (The New 52)	Manapul, Francis; Buccellato, Brian/Manapul, Francis	$16.99/ TP
18.	9781401242749/ OCT130243	The Flash Vol. 3: Gorilla Warfare (The New 52)	Manapul, Francis; Buccellato, Brian/Manapul, Francis	$24.99/ HC

JUSTICE LEAGUE BACKLIST AND SUGGESTED READING ORDER

	ISBN/Diamond Code	Title	Author/Artist	US$/Format
1.	9781401209322/ DEC050265	JLA: The Greatest Stories Ever Told	Various/ Various	$19.99/ HC
2.	9781401238353/ OCT120271	Showcase Presents: Justice League of America Vol. 6	Wein, Len/ Dillon, Dick	$19.99/ TP
3.	9781401212674/ OCT060211	Justice League of America: Hereby Elects	Various/ Various	$14.99/ TP
4.	9781401233143/ JUN110276	JLA Vol. 1	Morrison, Grant/ Porter, Howard	$19.99/ TP
5.	9781401235185/ APR120256	JLA Vol. 2	Morrison, Grant/ Porter, Howard	$24.99/ TP
6.	9781401238322/ OCT120267	JLA Vol. 3	Morrison, Grant/ Porter, Howard	$24.99/ TP
7.	9781401243852/ NOV130242	JLA Vol. 4	Morrison, Grant; Waid, Mark/ Porter, Howard; Pajarillo, Mark	$24.99/ TP

DC COMICS READING ORDER

	ISBN/Diamond Code	Title	Author/Artist	US$/Format
8.	9781401244101/ JUN130263	JLA Earth 2 Deluxe Edition	Morrison, Grant/ Quitely, Frank	$24.99/ HC
9.	9781401204587/ AUG118125	Identity Crisis	Meltzer, Brad/ Morales, Rags	$17.99/ TP
10.	9781401215804/ JUN080244	Justice League of America: The Tornado's Path, Vol. 1	Meltzer, Brad/ Benes, Ed	$17.99/ TP
11.	9781401218690/ OCT080173	Justice League of America: The Lightning Saga, Vol. 2	Meltzer, Brad/ Benes, Ed	$17.99/ TP
12.	9781401220501/ MAR090190	Justice League of America: The Injustice League	McDuffie, Dwayne/ Benes, Ed	$17.99/ TP
13.	9781401220105/ OCT090247	Justice League of America: Sanctuary	McDuffie, Dwayne/ Benes, Ed	$14.99/ TP
14.	9781401222536/ FEB100187	Justice League of America: The Second Coming	McDuffie, Dwayne/ Benes, Ed	$17.99/ TP
15.	9781401224233/ JUL100203	Justice League of America: When Worlds Collide	McDuffie, Dwayne/ Benes, Ed	$14.99/ TP
16.	9781401225643/ MAR110353	Justice League: Cry For Justice	Robinson, James/ Cascioli, Mauro	$19.99/ TP
17.	9781401230142/ DEC110290	Justice League: Rise and Fall	Krul, J.T./ Dallocchio, Federico	$17.99/ TP
18.	9781401232603/ JUN110277	Justice League of America: Team History	Robinson, James/ Bagley, Mark	$17.99/ TP
19.	9781401231934/ DEC110289	Justice League of America: Dark Things	Robinson, James/ Bagley, Mark	$17.99/ TP
20.	9781401232436/ MAY110247	Justice League of America: Omega	Robinson, James/ Bagley, Mark	$24.99/ TP
21.	9781401234133/ JUL120225	Justice League of America: The Rise of Eclipso	Robinson, James/ Booth, Brett	$22.99/ TP
22.	9781401237882/ OCT120252	Justice League Vol. 1: Origin (The New 52)	Johns, Geoff/ Lee, Jim	$16.99/ TP
23.	9781401237653/ JUN130261	Justice League Vol. 2: The Villain's Journey (The New 52)	Johns, Geoff/ Lee, Jim	$16.99/ TP
24.	9781401246983/ JAN140339	Justice League Vol. 3: Throne of Atlantis (The New 52)	Johns, Geoff/ Reis, Ivan; Daniel, Tony S.	$16.99/ TP
25.	9781401242367/ JUL130230	Justice League of America Vol. 1: World's Most Dangerous (The New 52)	Johns, Geoff/ Finch, David	$24.99/ HC
26.	9781401217396/ DEC080163	Justice League International Vol. 1	Giffen, Keith/ Maguire, Kevin	$17.99/ TP
27.	9781401220204/ APR090211	Justice League International Vol. 2	Giffen, Keith/ Maguire, Kevin	$17.99/ TP
28.	9781401225384/ AUG090174	Justice League International Vol. 3	Giffen, Keith/ Maguire, Kevin	$19.99/ TP

DC COMICS READING ORDER

	ISBN/Diamond Code	Title	Author/Artist	US$/Format
29.	9781401221973/ DEC090212	Justice League International Vol. 4	Giffen, Keith/ Maguire, Kevin	$17.99/ TP
30.	9781401230104/ OCT100269	Justice League International Vol. 5	Giffen, Keith/ Maguire, Kevin	$19.99/ TP
31.	9781401230203/ DEC100249	Justice League: Generation Lost Vol. 1	Winick, Judd/ Lopresti, Aaron	$39.99/ HC
32.	9781401235345/ FEB120250	Justice League International Vol.1: The Signal Masters (The New 52)	Jurgens, Dan/ Lopresti, Aaron	$14.99/ TP
33.	9781401237936/ OCT120255	Justice League International Vol. 2: Breakdown (The New 52)	Jurgens, Dan/ Lopresti, Aaron	$16.99/ TP
34.	9781401237042/ JUL120211	Justice League Dark Vol. 1: In The Dark (The New 52)	Milligan, Peter/ Janin, Mikel	$14.99/ TP
35.	9781401240240/ APR130217	Justice League Dark Vol. 2: The Books of Magic (The New 52)	Lemire, Jeff/ Janin, Mikel	$16.99/ TP
36.	9781401242459/ OCT130241	Justice League Dark Vol. 3: The Death of Magic (The New 52)	Lemire, Jeff	$16.99/ TP
37.	9781401247171/ DEC130297	Justice League Vol. 4: The Grid (The New 52)	Johns, Geoff/ Reis, Ivan	$24.99/ HC
38.	9781401245191/ NOV130226	Justice League: Trinity War (The New 52)	Johns, Geoff; Lemire, Jeff/ Reis, Ivan; Mahnke, Doug; Janin, Mikel	$29.99/ HC
39.	9781401203504/ FEB058027	DC: The New Frontier Vol. 1	Cooke, Darwyn/ Cooke, Darwyn	$19.99/ TP
40.	9781401204617/ FEB050272	DC: The New Frontier Vol. 2	Cooke, Darwyn/ Cooke, Darwyn	$19.99/ TP
41.	9781401245009/ JUL130242	Injustice: Gods Among Us Vol. 1	Taylor, Tom/ Raapack, Jheremy; Miller, Mike S.	$19.99 HC
42.	9781401246013/ FEB140260	Injustice: Gods Among Us Vol. 2	Tom Taylor/ Miller, Mike S.; Derenick, Tom	$19.99/ HC
43.	9781563894800/ MAR045122	Justice League of America: The Nail	Davis, Alan/ Davis, Alan	$14.95/ TP
44.	9781401235260/ MAR110354	Justice	Ross, Alex/ Ross, Alex	$29.99/ TP
45.	9781401220341/ SEP138294	Kingdom Come	Waid, Mark/ Ross, Alex	$19.99/ TP
46.	9781563895678/ APR068118	Kingdom	Waid, Mark/ Various	$19.99/ TP

WONDER WOMAN BACKLIST AND SUGGESTED READING ORDER

	ISBN/Diamond Code	Title	Author/Artist	US$/Format
1.	9781401238650/ JUL120228	Wonder Woman: The Amazon Princess Archives Vol. 1	Kanigher, Robert/ Andru, Ross	$75.00/ HC
2.	9781401212162/ JAN070323	Wonder Woman: The Greatest Stories Ever Told	Various/ Various	$19.99/ TP

DC COMICS READING ORDER

	ISBN/Diamond Code	Title	Author/Artist	US$/Format
3.	9781401234942/ APR120259	Wonder Woman: Twelve Labors	Various/ Various	$14.99/ TP
4.	9781401230784/ APR120258	Wonder Woman: Odyssey Vol. 1	Straczynski, J. Michael/ Kramer, Don	$14.99/ TP
5.	9781401234324/ NOV120274	Wonder Woman: Odyssey Vol. 2	Straczynski, J. Michael/ Kramer, Don	$14.99/ TP
6.	9781401234102/ DEC110279	Flashpoint: World of Flashpoint Featuring Wonder Woman	Various/ Various	$17.99/ TP
7.	9781401235628/ OCT120256	Wonder Woman Vol. 1: Blood (The New 52)	Azzarello, Brian/ Chiang, Cliff	$14.99/ TP
8.	9781401238100/ JUN130271	Wonder Woman Vol. 2: Guts (The New 52)	Azzarello, Brian/ Chiang, Cliff	$14.99/ TP
9.	9781401246075/ MAY130226	Wonder Woman Vol. 3: Iron (The New 52)	Azzarello, Brian/ Chiang, Cliff; Akins, Tony	$16.99/ TP
10.	9781401246082/ NOV130234	Wonder Woman Vol. 4: War (The New 52)	Azzarello, Brian/ Chiang, Cliff	$22.99/ HC

GREEN ARROW BACKLIST AND SUGGESTED READING ORDER

	ISBN/Diamond Code	Title	Author/Artist	US$/Format
1.	9781401231071/ MAR110355	The Jack Kirby Omnibus Vol. 1	Various/ Kirby, Jack	$49.99/ TP
2.	9781401217433/ JAN090227	Green Arrow: Year One	Diggle, Andy/ Jock	$14.99/ TP
3.	9781401235178/ MAY120290	Green Lantern/Green Arrow	O'Neil, Dennis/ Adams, Neal	$29.99/ TP
4.	9781401238629/ JUN120250	Green Arrow: The Longbow Hunters	Grell, Mike/ Grell, Mike	$14.99/ TP
5.	9781401243265/ AUG130304	Green Arrow Vol. 1: Hunter's Moon	Grell, Mike; Giordano, Dick/ Hannigan, Ed	$14.99/ TP
6.	9781401200442/ JUN120251	Green Arrow: The Archer's Quest	Meltzer, Brad/ Hester, Phil	$14.99/ TP
7.	9781401235284/ NOV120266	Green Arrow: Salvation	Krul, J.T./Neves, Diogenes; Cifuentes, Vincente	$16.99/ TP
8.	9781401234867/ FEB120249	Green Arrow Vol. 1: The Midas Touch (The New 52)	Krul, J.T./ Perez, George	$14.99/ TP
9.	9781401238421/ OCT120254	Green Arrow Vol. 2: Triple Threat (The New 52)	Nocenti, Ann/ Tolibao, Harvey	$14.99/ TP
10.	9781401244057/ JUN130266	Green Arrow Vol. 3: Harrow (The New 52)	Nocenti, Ann/ Williams II, Freddie	$14.99/ TP
11.	9781401246907/ DEC130306	Green Arrow Vol. 4: The Kill Machine (The New 52)	Lemire, Jeff/ Sorrentino, Andrea	$16.99/ TP
12.	9781401242992/ JUN130265	Arrow Vol. 1	Guggenheim, Marc; Kreisberg, Andrew/Grell, Mike	$16.99/ TP

DC COMICS READING ORDER

	ISBN/Diamond Code	Title	Author/Artist	US$/Format
13.	9781401246037/ JAN140347	Arrow Vol. 2	Various/ Various	$16.99/ TP

JUSTICE SOCIETY OF AMERICA BACKLIST AND SUGGESTED READING ORDER

	ISBN/Diamond Code	Title	Author/Artist	US$/Format
1.	9781401215859/ JUL080163	Justice Society America: The Next Age, Vol. 1	Johns, Geoff/ Eaglesham, Dale	$14.99/ TP
2.	9781401217419/ JAN090231	Justice Society of America: Thy Kingdom Come Part I	Johns, Geoff/ Eaglesham, Dale	$14.99/ TP
3.	9781401219468/ AUG090175	Justice Society of America: Thy Kingdom Come Part II	Johns, Geoff/ Eaglesham, Dale	$19.99/ TP
4.	9781401221676/ JAN100298	Justice Society of America: Thy Kingdom Come Part III	Johns, Geoff/ Eaglesham, Dale	$19.99/ TP
5.	9781401225315/ JUN100206	Justice Society of America: Black Adam & Isis	Johns, Geoff/ Ordway, Jerry	$14.99/ TP
6.	9781401227142/ FEB100189	Justice Society of America: The Bad Seed	Willingham, Bill/ Merino, Jesus	$14.99/ TP
7.	9781401229016/ SEP100251	Justice Society of America: Axis of Evil	Willingham, Bill/ Merino, Jesus	$14.99/ TP
8.	9781401232849/ JUN110279	Justice Society of America: Supertown	Guggenheim, Marc/ Kolins, Scott	$14.99/ TP
9.	9781401233686/ NOV110205	Justice Society of America: Monument Park	Guggenheim, Marc/ Derenick, Tom	$14.99/ TP
10.	9781401235000/ MAR120247	Mister Terrific Vol. 1: Mind Games	Wallace, Eric/ Gugliotta, Gianluca	$14.99/ TP
11.	9781401242817/ JUL130241	Earth 2 Vol. 1: The Gathering (The New 52)	Robinson, James/ Scott, Nicola	$14.99/ TP
12.	9781401246143/ JAN140344	Earth 2 Vol. 2: Tower of Fate (The New 52)	Robinson, James/ Scott, Nicola	$16.99/ TP
13.	9781401246150/ DEC130299	Earth 2 Vol. 3: War (The New 52)	Robinson, James/ Scott, Nicola	$22.99/ HC
14.	9781401242510/ JUL130243	JSA Liberty Files: The Whistling Skull	Moore, B. Clay/ Harris, Tony	$14.99/ TP

LEGION OF SUPER HEROES BACKLIST AND SUGGESTED READING ORDER

	ISBN/Diamond Code	Title	Author/Artist	US$/Format
1.	9781401237301/ JUL120224	Legion: Secret Origin	Levitz, Paul/ Bautista, Chris	$14.99/ TP
2.	9781401244163/ NOV130243	The Legion of Super-Heroes: The Great Darkness Saga	Levitz, Paul/ Giffen, Keith	$24.99/ TP
3.	9781401230982/ APR110207	Legion of Super-Heroes: The Curse Deluxe Edition	Various/ Various	$49.99/ HC
4.	9781401219444/ SEP080174	Legion of Super-Heroes: The More Things Change	Levitz, Paul/ Giffen, Keith	$17.99/ TP

DC COMICS READING ORDER

	ISBN/Diamond Code	Title	Author/Artist	US$/Format
5.	9781401231200/ FEB110204	Legion Lost	Abnett, Dan/ Coipel, Olivier	$39.99/ HC
6.	9781401223250/ JUL100195	Final Crisis: Legion of 3 Worlds	Johns, Geoff/ Pérez, George	$14.99/ TP
7.	9781401231682/ FEB110203	Superboy and The Legion of Super-Heroes: Early Years	Levitz, Paul/ Pansica, Eduardo	$14.99/ TP
8.	9781401219048/ APR090217	Superman and The Legion of Super-Heroes	Johns, Geoff/ Frank, Gary	$14.99/ TP
9.	9781401220181/ JUL090236	Legion of Super-Heroes: Enemy Rising	Shooter, Jim/ Lopresti, Aaron	$14.99/ TP
10.	9781401223052/ FEB100190	Legion of Super-Heroes: Enemy Manifest	Shooter, Jim/ Manapul, Francis	$14.99/ TP
11.	9781401230395/ DEC100250	Legion of Super-Heroes Vol. 1: The Choice	Levitz, Paul/ Cinar, Yildiray	$24.99/ TP
12.	9781401232382/ MAY110251	Legion of Super-Heroes Vol. 2: Consequences	Levitz, Paul/ Cinar, Yildiray	$24.99/ TP
13.	9781401233679/ JAN120311	Legion of Super-Heroes: When Evil Calls	Levitz, Paul/ Cinar, Yildiray	$29.99/ TP
14.	9781401237035/ JUN120238	Legion Lost Vol. 1: Run From Tomorrow (The New 52)	Nicieza, Fabian/ Woods, Pete	$14.99/ TP
15.	9781401240257/ MAY130223	Legion Lost Vol. 2: The Culling (The New 52)	Defalco, Tom/Woods, Pete; Guinaldo, Andres	$16.99/ TP
16.	9781401235017/ MAR120246	Legion of Super-Heroes Vol. 1: Hostile World (The New 52)	Levitz, Paul/ Portela, Francis	$14.99/ TP
17.	9781401240974/ FEB130213	Marc Legion of Super-Heroes Vol. 2: The Dominators (The New 52)	Levitz, Paul/Portela, Francis; Kolins, Scott	$16.99/ TP
18.	9781401243326/ NOV130232	Legion of Super-Heroes Vol. 3: The Fatal Five (The New 52)	Levitz, Paul/ Giffen, Keith; Kolins, Scott	$16.99/ TP

TEEN TITANS BACKLIST AND SUGGESTED READING ORDER

	ISBN/Diamond Code	Title	Author/Artist	US$/Format
1.	9781401234294/ DEC110292	New Teen Titans Omnibus Vol. 2	Wolfman, Marv/ Pérez, George	$75.00/ HC
2.	9781401238452/ JAN130313	The New Teen Titans Omnibus Vol. 3	Wolfman, Marv/ Pérez, George	$75.00/ HC
3.	9781401203191/ NOV120275	The New Teen Titans: Games	Wolfman, Marv/ Pérez, George	$16.99/ TP
4.	9781401241056/ APR130220	The Silver Age Teen Titans Archives Vol. 2	Haney, Bob/ Cardy, Nick	$75.00/ HC
5.	9781401236939/ SEP120242	Teen Titans by Geoff Johns Omnibus	Johns, Geoff/ Various	$150.00/ HC
6.	9781401236984/ JUN120239	Teen Titans Vol. 1: It's Our Right To Fight (The New 52)	Lobdell, Scott/ Booth, Brett	$14.99/ TP

DC COMICS SELECTED BACKLIST

	ISBN/Diamond Code	Title	Author/Artist	US$/Format
7.	9781401241032/ MAR130272	Teen Titans Vol. 2: The Culling (The New 52)	Lobdell, Scott/ Booth, Brett	$16.99/ TP
8.	9781401243210/ SEP130274	Teen Titans Vol. 3: Death of the Family (The New 52)	Lobdell, Scott/ Booth, Brett	$14.99/ TP

DC COMICS SELECTED BACKLIST

DC	9781401235567/ JUL120217	52 Omnibus	Various/Various	$150.00/ HC
DC	9781401240301/ JAN130305	The Authority Vol. 1	Ellis, Warren/ Hitch, Bryan	$29.99/ TP
DC	9781401242756/ AUG130305	The Authority Vol. 2	Millar, Mark/ Quitely, Frank	$34.99/ HC
DC	9781401237097/ JUL120213	All-Star Western Vol. 1: Guns and Gotham (The New 52)	Gray, Justin; Palmiotti, Jimmy/Moritat	$16.99/ TP
DC	9781401238513/ DEC120325	All-Star Western Vol. 2: The War of Lords and Owls (The New 52)	Palmiotti, Jimmy; Gray, Justin/Moritat	$16.99/ TP
DC	9781401243999/ AUG130300	All-Star Western Vol. 3: The Black Diamond Probability (The New 52)	Palmiotti, Jimmy; Gray, Justin/Moritat	$16.99/ TP
DC	9781401235079/ FEB120247	Animal Man Vol. 1: The Hunt	Lemire, Jeff/ Foreman, Travel	$14.99/ TP
DC	9781401238001/ OCT120251	Animal Man Vol. 2: Animal vs. Man (The New 52)	Lemire, Jeff/ Pugh, Steve; Green, Timothy	$16.99/ TP
DC	9781401242626/ JUN130267	Animal Man Vol. 3: Rotworld: The Red Kingdom (The New 52)	Lemire, Jeff; Snyder, Scott/ Pugh, Steve	$16.99/ TP
DC	9781401231132/ MAR110349	Aquaman: Death of the Prince	Various/ Various	$29.99/ TP
DC	9781401237103/ FEB130206	Aquaman Vol. 1: The Trench (The New 52)	Johns, Geoff/ Reis, Ivan	$14.99/ TP
DC	9781401242954/ AUG130295	Aquaman Vol. 2: The Others (The New 52)	Johns, Geoff/ Reis, Ivan	$14.99/ TP
DC	9781401246952/ FEB140252	Aquaman Vol. 3: Throne of Atlantis	Johns, Geoff/ Pelletier, Paul; Reis, Ivan	$14.99/ TP
DC	9781401246969/ JAN140337	Aquaman Vol. 4: Death of A King (The New 52)	Johns, Geoff/ Pelletier, Paul	$24.99/ HC
DC	9781401229245/ SEP100247	Batgirl: The Greatest Stories Ever Told	Various/ Various	$19.99/ TP
DC	9781401240332/ MAR130279	Batgirl/Robin Year One	Dixon, Chuck/ Beatty, Scott; Martin, Marcos	$24.99/ TP
DC	9781401238148/ NOV120261	Batgirl Vol. 1: The Darkest Reflection (The New 52)	Simone, Gail/ Syaf, Ardian	$14.99/ TP
DC	9781401238179/ JUL130236	Batgirl Vol. 2: Knightfall Descends (The New 52)	Simone, Gail/ Syaf, Ardian; Benes, Ed	$16.99/ TP

DC COMICS SELECTED BACKLIST

	ISBN/Diamond Code	Title	Author/Artist	US$/Format
DC	9781401246280/ FEB140247	Batgirl Vol. 3: Death of the Family (The New 52)	Simone, Gail/Sampere, Daniel; Benes, Ed	$16.99/ TP
DC	9781401246297/ JAN140355	Batgirl Vol. 4: Wanted (The New 52)	Simone, Gail/ Pasarin, Fernando	$24.99/ HC
DC	9781401234768/ APR120246	Batwing Vol. 1: The Lost King-dom (The New 52)	Winick, Judd/ Oliver, Ben	$14.99/ TP
DC	9781401237912/ DEC120327	Batwing Vol. 2: In The Shadow of the Ancients (The New 52)	Winick, Judd/ To, Marcus	$14.99/ TP
DC	9781401244033/ OCT130237	Batwing Vol. 3: Enemy of the State (The New 52)	Winick, Judd; Nicieza, Fabian/To, Marcus	$14.99/ TP
DC	9781401231460/ MAR110341	Batwoman: Elegy	Rucka, Greg/ Williams III, J.H.	$17.99/ TP
DC	9781401237844/ OCT120253	Batwoman Vol. 1: Hydrology (The New 52)	Williams III, J.H.; Blackman, W. Haden	$14.99/ TP
DC	9781401237929/ JUN130269	Batwoman Vol. 2: To Drown the World (The New 52)	Williams III, J.H.; Blackman, W. Haden/Reeder, Amy; McCarthy, Trevor	$14.99/ TP
DC	9781401242466/ MAY130225	Batwoman Vol. 3: World's Finest (The New 52)	Williams III, J.H.; Blackman, W. Haden	$22.99/ HC
DC	9781401234492/ JUL120221	Birds of Prey Vol. 2: Death of Oracle	Simone, Gail/ Various	$16.99/ TP
DC	9781401236991/ JUN120236	Birds of Prey Vol. 1: Trouble In Mind (The New 52)	Swierczynski, Duane/ Saiz, Jesus	$14.99/ TP
DC	9781401238131/ JAN130297	Birds of Prey Vol. 2: Your Kiss Might Kill (The New 52)	Swierczynski, Duane/ Foreman, Travel; Saiz, Jesus	$14.99/ TP
DC	9781401244040/ SEP130270	Birds of Prey Vol. 3: A Clash of Daggers (The New 52)	Swierczynski, Duane/ Molenaar, Romano	$14.99/ TP
DC	9781401237141/ AUG120247	Blackhawks Vol. 1: The Great Leap Forward (The New 52)	Costa, Mike/ Nolan, Graham	$16.99/ TP
DC	9781401237134/ AUG120246	Blue Beetle Vol. 1: Metamorphosis (The New 52)	Bedard, Tony/ Guara, Ig	$14.99/ TP
DC	9781401238506/ JAN130299	Blue Beetle Vol. 2: Blue Diamond (The New 52)	Bedard, Tony/ Guara, Ig	$16.99/ HC
DC	9781401220068/ FEB090201	Booster Gold: 52 Pick Up	Johns, Geoff/ Jurgens, Dan	$14.99/ TP
DC	9781401220143/ SEP090164	Booster Gold: Blue and Gold	Johns, Geoff/ Jurgens, Dan	$14.99/ TP
DC	9781401230241/ JAN110325	Booster Gold: Past Imperfect	Giffen, Keith/ Olliffe, Patrick	$17.99/ TP
DC	9781401226435/ JAN100297	Booster Gold: Day of Death	Giffen, Keith/ Olliffe, Patrick	$14.99/ TP
DC	9781401222499/ MAY090181	Booster Gold: Reality Lost	Jurgens, Dan/ Jurgens, Dan	$14.99/ TP

DC COMICS SELECTED BACKLIST

	ISBN/Diamond Code	Title	Author/Artist	US$/Format
DC	9781401229184/ SEP100248	Booster Gold: The Tomorrow Memory	Jurgens, Dan/ Jurgens, Dan	$17.99/ TP
DC	9781401240363/ APR130228	Camelot 3000	Barr, Mike W./ Bolland, Brian	$19.99/ TP
DC	9781401237158/ AUG120250	Captain Atom Vol. 1: Evolution (The New 52)	Krul, J.T./ Williams II, Freddie	$14.99/ TP
DC	9781401240998/ MAY130222	Captain Atom Vol. 2: Genesis (The New 52)	Krul, J.T./ Williams II, Freddie	$19.99/ TP
DC	9781401207175/ MAY098043	Catwoman: When In Rome	Loeb, Jeph/ Sale, Tim	$14.99/ TP
DC	9781401233846/ OCT110246	Catwoman Vol. 1	Brubaker, Ed/ Cooke, Darwyn	$29.99/ TP
DC	9781401240370/ MAR130271	Catwoman Vol. 2: No Easy Way Down	Brubaker, Ed/ Stewart, Cameron	$14.99/ TP
DC	9781401234645/ FEB120248	Catwoman Vol. 1: The Game (The New 52)	Winick, Judd/ March, Guillem	$14.99/ TP
DC	9781401238391/ NOV120260	Catwoman Vol. 2: Dollhouse (The New 52)	Winick, Judd/ March, Guillem	$14.99/ TP
DC	9781401242725/ JUL130237	Catwoman Vol. 3: Death of the Family (The New 52)	Nocenti, Ann/ Sandoval, Rafa	$24.99/ TP
DC	9781401234744/ FEB120263	Challengers of the Unknown Omnibus by Jack Kirby	Various/ Kirby, Jack	$39.99/ HC
DC	9781401243234/ NOV130227	Constantine Vol. 1: The Spark and The Flame (The New 52)	Lemire, Jeff; Fawkes, Ray/ Guedes, Renato	$9.99/ TP
DC	9781401243821/ SEP130281	Creature Commandos	Various/ Various	$14.99/ TP
DC	9781401225919/ OCT090244	The Creeper by Steve Ditko	Various/ Ditko, Steve	$39.99/ HC
DC	9781563898952/ OCT098268	Crisis On Multiple Earths Vol. 1	Fox, Gardner/ Sekowsky, Mike	$14.99/ TP
DC	9781401200039/ APR058270	Crisis On Multiple Earths Vol. 2	Fox, Gardner/ Sekowsky, Mike	$14.99/ TP
DC	9781401202316/ MAY040298	Crisis On Multiple Earths Vol. 3	Friedrich, Mike/ Sekowsky, Mike	$14.99/ TP
DC	9781401209575/ FEB060261	Crisis On Multiple Earths Vol. 4	Various/ Dillin, Dick	$14.99/ TP
DC	9781401226237/ JAN100301	Crisis On Multiple Earths Vol. 5	Conway, Gerry/ Pérez, George; Dillin, Dick	$14.99/ TP
DC	9781401238223/ MAR130278	Crisis On Multiple Earths Vol. 6	Conway, Gerry/ Pérez, George	$19.99/ TP
DC	9781401237998/ OCT120250	The Culling: Rise of the Ravagers (The New 52)	Defalco, Tom; Lobdell, Scott /Various	$16.99/ TP

DC COMICS SELECTED BACKLIST

	ISBN/Diamond Code	Title	Author/Artist	US$/Format
DC	9781401237950/ DEC120330	Day of Judgment	Johns, Geoff/ Smith, Matt	$19.99/ TP
DC	9781401242435/ JUN130262	DC Comics One Million Omnibus	Morrison, Grant/ Various	$99.99/ TP
DC	9781401238841/ AUG120249	The New 52 Zero Omnibus (The New 52)	Various/ Various	$99.99/ HC
DC	9781401244965/ AUG130289	DC New 52 Villains Omnibus (The New 52)	Various/ Various	$150.00/ HC
DC	9781401219178/ JUN080241	DC Universe Illustrated by Neal Adams Vol. 1	Various/ Adams, Neal	$39.99/ HC
DC	9781401237165/ AUG120251	DC Universe Presents Vol. 1 Featuring Deadman & Challengers of the Unknown (The New 52)	Jenkins, Paul/ Chang, Bernard	$16.99/ TP
DC	9781401240769/ MAY130227	DC Universe Presents Vol. 2: Vandal Savage (The New 52)	Various/ Various	$14.99/ TP
DC	9781401242770/ NOV130230	DC Universe Presents Vol. 3: Black Lightning and Blue Devil (The New 52)	Andreyko, Marc/ Rocha, Robson	$14.99/ TP
DC	9781401226466/ NOV090173	DC Universe: Origins	Various/ Various	$14.99/ TP
DC	9781401234041/ JAN130303	DC Universe Secret Origins	Various/ Various	$14.99/ TP
DC	9781401233402/ DEC120333	DC Universe by Alan Moore	Moore, Alan/ Various	$24.99/ TP
DC	9781401231347/ FEB120262	DC Universe: Legacies	Wein, Len/ Various	$24.99/ TP
DC	9781401231163/ FEB110198	Deadman Vol. 1	Various/ Adams, Neal	$19.99/ TP
DC	9781401233884/ NOV110199	Deadman Vol. 2	Various/ Adams, Neal	$14.99/ TP
DC	9781401237288/ SEP120236	Deadman Vol. 3	Levitz, Paul/ Various	$16.99/ TP
DC	9781401243241/ SEP130282	Deadman Book Four	Wein, Len/Aparo, Jim; Garcia-Lopez, Jose Luis	$14.99/ TP
DC	9781401242985/ JUL130244	Deadshot: Beginnings	Ostrander, John/ Yale, Kim; McDonnell, Luke	$14.99/ TP
DC	9781401234812/ MAY120282	Deathstroke Vol. 1: Legacy (The New 52)	Higgins, Kyle/ Bennet, Joe	$16.99/ TP
DC	9781401240387/ NOV130231	Deathstroke Vol. 2: Lobo Hunt (The New 52)	Liefeld, Rob/ Liefeld, Rob	$19.99/ TP
DC	9781401242503/ OCT130251	The Demon: From The Darkness	Wagner, Matt/ Various	$14.99/ TP
DC	9781401234720/ APR120247	Demon Knights Vol. 1: Seven Against The Dark (The New 52)	Cornell, Paul/ Neves, Diogenes	$14.99/ TP

DC COMICS SELECTED BACKLIST

	ISBN/Diamond Code	Title	Author/Artist	US$/Format
DC	9781401240394/ FEB130208	Demon Knights Vol. 2: The Avalon Trap (The New 52)	Cornell, Paul/ Neves, Diogenes	$14.99/ TP
DC	9781401242695/ OCT130242	Demon Knights Vol. 3: The Gathering Storm (The New 52)	Cornell, Paul/Venditti, Robert; Chang, Bernard	$19.99/ TP
DC	9781401244972/ APR130243	Diablo: Sword of Justice	Williams, Aaron/ Lacroix, Joseph	$14.99/ TP
DC	9781401237752/ NOV130249	Dial H Vol. 1: Into You (The New 52)	Miéville, China/ Santolouco, Mateus	$14.99/ TP
DC	9781401243838/ NOV130228	Dial H Vol. 2: Exchange (The New 52)	Miéville, China/Ponticelli, Alberto; Green, Dan	$16.99/ TP
DC	9781401243258/ SEP130283	Doctor Mid-Nite	Wagner, Matt/ Snyder, John K.	$14.99/ TP
DC	9781401242817/ JUL130241	Earth 2 Vol. 1: The Gathering (The New 52)	Robinson, James/ Scott, Nicola	$14.99/ TP
DC	9781401246143/ JAN140344	Earth 2 Vol. 2: The Tower of Fate (The New 52)	Robinson, James/ Scott, Nicola; Cinar, Yildiray	$16.99/ TP
DC	9781401222826/ FEB090203	Final Crisis	Morrison, Grant/ Jones, J.G.	$19.99/ TP
DC	9781401223250/ JUL100195	Final Crisis: Legion of 3 Worlds	Johns, Geoff/ Pérez, George	$14.99/ TP
DC	9781401223236/ MAY100186	Final Crisis: Revelations	Rucka, Greg/ Tan, Philip	$14.99/ TP
DC	9781401231835/ APR110202	Firestorm: The Nuclear Man	Conway, Gerry/ Milgrom, Al	$17.99/ TP
DC	9781401237004/ JUN120237	The Fury of Firestorm: The Nuclear Men Vol. 1: God Particle (The New 52)	Van Sciver, Ethan/ Cinar, Yildiray	$14.99/ TP
DC	9781401240325/ MAR130275	The Fury of Firestorm: The Nuclear Men Vol. 2: The Firestorm Protocols (The New 52)	Harris, Joe/Van Sciver, Ethan; Cinar, Yildiray	$14.99/ TP
DC	9781401242923/ SEP130272	The Fury of Firestorm: The Nuclear Men Vol. 3: Takeover (The New 52)	Jurgens, Dan/ Jurgens, Dan	$16.99/ TP
DC	9781401234713/ MAR120244	Frankenstein, Agent of S.H.A.D.E. Vol. 1: War of the Monsters (The New 52)	Lemire, Jeff/ Ponticelli, Alberto	$14.99/ TP
DC	9781401238186/ JAN130298	Frankenstein Agent of S.H.A.D.E. Vol. 2: Secrets of the Dead (The New 52)	Kindt, Matt; Lemire, Jeff/ Ponticelli, Alberto	$16.99/ TP
DC	9781401238537/ DEC120328	G.I. Combat Vol. 1: The War That Time Forgot (The New 52)	Krul, J.T./ Panosian, Dan	$19.99/ TP
DC	9781401236960/ SEP130280	Gears of War Book Three	Traviss, Karen/ Mhan, Pop	$19.99/ TP
DC	9781401220372/ DEC100248	Gotham Central Book 1: In The Line of Duty	Rucka, Greg/ Lark, Michael	$19.99/ TP
DC	9781401225438/ APR110203	Gotham Central Book 2: Jokers and Madmen	Rucka, Greg/ Lark, Michael	$19.99/ TP

DC COMICS SELECTED BACKLIST

	ISBN/Diamond Code	Title	Author/Artist	US$/Format
DC	9781401232320/ JUL110257	Gotham Central Book 3: On The Freak Beat	Rucka, Greg/ Lark, Michael	$19.99/ TP
DC	9781401231941/ JAN120307	Gotham Central Book 4: Corrigan	Rucka, Greg/ Kano	$19.99/ TP
DC	9781401234973/ APR120248	Grifter Vol. 1: Most Wanted	Edmondson, Nathan/ Cafu	$14.99/ TP
DC	9781401240981/ FEB130209	Grifter Vol. 2: New Found Power (The New 52)	Liefeld, Rob; Tieri, Frank/ Clark, Scott	$16.99/ TP
DC	9781401237943/ OCT120266	Hard Time: Sixteen	Gerber, Steve/ Hurtt, Brian	$14.99/ TP
DC	9781401239107/ MAR130252	Harlan Ellison's 7 Against Chaos	Ellison, Harlan/ Chadwick, Paul	$24.99/ HC
DC	9781401240417/ MAR130276	Harley Quinn: Night and Day	Kesel, Karl/ Dodson, Terry; Woods, Pete	$16.99/ TP
DC	9781401216573/ NOV110200	Harley Quinn: Preludes and Knock Knock Jokes	Kesel, Karl/Dodson, Terry	$19.99/ TP
DC	9781401245955/ DEC130313	Harley Quinn: Welcome to Metropolis	Kesel, Karl/Dodson, Terry	$19.99/ TP
DC	NOV110200	Hawk & Dove: Ghosts & Demons	Kesel, Karl/ Liefeld, Rob	$14.99/ TP
DC	9781401234980/ MAY120281	Hawk and Dove Vol. 1: First Strikes (The New 52)	Gates, Sterling/ Liefeld, Rob	$16.99/ TP
DC	9781401232221/ SEP110186	Hawkman Omnibus Vol. 1	Johns, Geoff/ Morales, Rags	$75.00/ HC
DC	9781401240226/ APR130245	He-Man and The Masters of the Universe Vol. 1	Robinson, James; Giffen, Keith/Tan, Philip	$14.99/ TP
DC	9781563897986/ FEB090206	History of the DC Universe	Wolfman, Marv/ Various	$12.99/ TP
DC	9781563893148/ MAR090185	Hitman Vol. 1: A Rage In Arkham	Ennis, Garth/ McCrea, John	$14.99/ TP
DC	9781401218423/ NOV090172	Hitman Vol. 2: Ten Thousand Bullets	Ennis, Garth/ McCrea, John	$17.99/ TP
DC	9781401228934/ SEP100252	Hitman Vol. 3: Local Heroes	Ennis, Garth/ McCrea, John	$17.99/ TP
DC	9781401230043/ JAN110327	Hitman Vol. 4: Ace of Killers	Ennis, Garth/ McCrea, John	$17.99/ TP
DC	9781401231187/ SEP110183	Hitman Vol. 5: Tommy's Heroes	Ennis, Garth/ McCrea, John	$29.99/ TP
DC	9781401232825/ JAN120309	Hitman Vol. 6: For Tomorrow	Ennis, Garth/ McCrea, John	$29.99/ TP
DC	9781401234003/ MAY120294	Hitman Vol. 7: Closing Time	Ennis, Garth/ McCrea, John	$29.99/ TP

DC COMICS SELECTED BACKLIST

	ISBN/Diamond Code	Title	Author/Artist	US$/Format
DC	9781401237332/ JUL120223	Huntress: Crossbow At The Crossroads (The New 52)	Levitz, Paul/ To, Marcus	$14.99/ TP
DC	9781401233716/ NOV110204	I, Vampire	Dematteis, Mark/ J. Sutton, Thomas	$29.99/ TP
DC	9781401236878/ JUL120212 I,	Vampire Vol. 1: Tainted Love (The New 52)	Fialkov, Joshua Hale/Sorrentino, Andrea	$14.99/ TP
DC	9781401237837/ DEC120326	I, Vampire Vol. 2: Rise of the Vampires (The New 52)	Fialkov, Joshua Hale/ Sorrentino, Andrea	$16.99/ TP
DC	9781401242787/ JUL130238	I, Vampire Vol. 3: Wave of Mutilation (The New 52)	Fialkov, Joshua Hale/Sorrentino, Andrea	$16.99/ TP
DC	9781401210601/ FEB118149	Infinite Crisis	Johns, Geoff/ Jimenez, Phil	$17.99/ TP
DC	9781401209223/ JUL060154	Infinite Crisis Companion	Rucka, Greg/ Various	$14.99/ TP
DC	9781401231057/ FEB110201	Infinity Inc.: The Generations Saga Vol. 1	Thomas, Roy/ Ordway, Jerry	$39.99/ HC
DC	9781401245009/ FEB130220	Injustice: Gods Among Us Vol. 1	Taylor, Tom/Raapack, Jheremy; Miller, Mike S.	$19.99/ HC
DC	9781401246013/ FEB140260	Injustice: Gods Among Us Vol. 2	Tom Taylor/Miller, Mike S.; Derenick, Tom	$19.99/ HC
DC	9781401240790/ FEB130220	In The Days of the Mob	Kirby, Jack/ Kirby, Jack	$39.99/ HC
DC	9781401232412/ AUG110250	Jack Kirby's Fourth World Omnibus Vol. 1	Kirby, Jack/ Kirby, Jack	$39.99/ TP
DC	9781401234409/ JAN120310	Jack Kirby's Fourth World Omnibus Vol. 2	Kirby, Jack/ Kirby, Jack	$29.99/ TP
DC	9781401235352/ MAY120295	Jack Kirby's Fourth World Omnibus Vol. 3	Kirby, Jack/ Kirby, Jack	$29.99/ TP
DC	9781401237462/ SEP120240	Jack Kirby's 4th World Omnibus Vol. 4	Kirby, Jack/ Kirby, Jack	$29.99/ TP
DC	9781401238339/ DEC120331	The Jack Kirby Omnibus Vol. 2	Kirby, Jack/ Kirby, Jack	$39.99/ HC
DC	978-1401240424/ MAY130232	Jack Kirby's O.M.A.C.	Kirby, Jack/ Kirby, Jack	$19.99/ TP
DC	9781401219161/ JUL080159	Jack Kirby's The Demon	Kirby, Jack/ Kirby, Jack	$49.99/ HC
DC	9781401243302/ AUG130306	Joe Kubert Presents	Kubert, Joe; Glanzman, Sam/Kubert, Joe	$19.99/ TP
DC	9781401242589/ AUG130307	The Joker: The Clown Prince of Crime	Various/ Various	$16.99/ TP
DC	9781401210953/ JUN060192	Jonah Hex	Gray, Justin; Palmiotti, Jimmy/Ross, Luke	$12.99/ TP

DC COMICS SELECTED BACKLIST

	ISBN/Diamond Code	Title	Author/Artist	US$/Format
DC	9781401227579/ FEB100186	Jonah Hex: Welcome to Paradise	Albano, John/ Various	$17.99/ TP
DC	9781401212490/ JAN070305	Jonah Hex: Guns of Vengeance	Gray, Justin; Palmiotti, Jimmy/Ross, Luke Ross, Luke	$12.99/ TP
DC	9781401214906/ JUN098462	Jonah Hex: Origins	Gray, Justin; Palmiotti, Jimmy/Various	$14.99/ TP
DC	9781401228996/ JUL100196	Jonah Hex: Counting Corpses	Gray, Justin; Palmiotti, Jimmy/Various	$14.99/ TP
DC	9781401230098/ JAN110330	Jonah Hex: Tall Tales	Gray, Justin; Palmiotti, Jimmy/Various	$14.99/ TP
DC	9781401232498/ AUG110248	Jonah Hex: Bury Me In Hell	Gray, Justin; Palmiotti, Jimmy/Various	$17.99/ TP
DC	9781401225513/ FEB110207	Jonah Hex: No Way Back	Gray, Justin; Palmiotti, Jimmy/Dezuniga, Tony	$14.99/ TP
DC	9781401243975/ AUG130308	The Judas Coin	Simonson, Walt/ Simonson, Walt	$14.99/ TP
DC	9781401238858/ AUG130309	Just Imagine Stan Lee Creating The DC Universe Omnibus	Lee, Stan/ Various	$75.00/ HC
DC	9781401236724/ AUG120257	Kamandi, The Last Boy on Earth Omnibus Vol. 2	Kirby, Jack/ Kirby, Jack	$49.99/ HC
DC	9781401216696/ JUN120247	Lobo: Portrait of a Bastich	Giffen, Keith/ Bisley, Simon	$19.99/ TP
DC	9781401243869/ NOV130245	Martian Manhunter: Son of Mars	Ostrander, John/ Mandrake, Tom	$19.99/ TP
DC	9781401243883/ NOV130246	Showcase Presents: Men of War	Various/ Various	$19.99/ TP
DC	9781401234997/ APR120249	Men of War Vol. 1: Uneasy Company (The New 52)	Brandon, Ivan/ Derenick, Tom	$19.99/ TP
DC	9781401238674/ AUG120258	The Metal Men Archives Vol. 2	Kanigher, Robert/ Andru, Ross	$75.00/ HC
DC	9781401245030/ JUN130270	Necessary Evil: Super-Villains of DC Comics	Various/ Various	$16.99/ TP
DC	9781401240448/ MAY130230	Nightwing: Old Friends, New Enemies	Wolfman, Marv/ Various	$14.99/ TP
DC	9781401237059/ JUL120214	Nightwing Vol. 1: Traps and Trapezes (The New 52)	Higgins, Kyle/ Barrows, Eddy	$14.99/ TP
DC	9781401240271/ APR130225	Nightwing Vol. 2: Night of the Owls (The New 52)	Higgins, Kyle/ Barrows, Eddy	$14.99/ TP
DC	9781401244132/ SEP130273	Nightwing Vol. 3: Death of the Family (The New 52)	Higgins, Kyle/ Barrows, Eddy	$16.99/ TP
DC	9781401234829/ MAY120283	O.M.A.C. Vol. 1: Omactivate! (The New 52)	Didio, Dan/ Giffen, Keith	$16.99/ TP

DC COMICS SELECTED BACKLIST

	ISBN/Diamond Code	Title	Author/Artist	US$/Format
DC	9781401237325/ JUN120249	Penguin: Pain and Prejudice	Hurwitz, Gregg/ Kudranski, Szymon	$14.99/ TP
DC	9781401242381/ SEP130279	The Planetary Omnibus	Ellis, Warren/ Cassaday, John	$75.00/ HC
DC	9781563896484/ FEB068129	Planetary Vol.1: All Over The World and Other Stories	Ellis, Warren/ Cassaday, John	$14.99/ TP
DC	9781563897641/ JAN068213	Planetary Vol. 2: The Fourth Man	Ellis, Warren/ Cassaday, John	$14.99/ TP
DC	9781401202941/ JAN050354	Planetary Vol. 3: Leaving The 20th Century	Ellis, Warren/ Cassaday, John	$14.99/ TP
DC	9781401223458/ SEP100285	Planetary Vol. 4: Spacetime Archeology	Ellis, Warren/ Cassaday, John	$17.99/ TP
DC	9781401243074/ NOV130247	Power Girl: Power Trip	Palmiotti, Jimmy; Johns, Geoff/Conner, Amanda	$29.99/ TP
DC	9781401240912/ FEB130211	The Ravagers Vol. 1: The Kids From N.O.W.H.E.R.E. (The New 52)	Mackie, Howard/ Churchill, Ian	$16.99/ TP
DC	9781401243135/ NOV130233	The Ravagers Vol. 2: Heavenly Destruction (The New 52)	Nelson, Michael Alan/ Guara, Ig	$14.99/ TP
DC	9781401223465/ MAR090211	Red	Ellis, Warren/ Plunkett, Killian	$14.99/ TP
DC	9781401231972/ JAN110413	Red: Better Red Than Dead	Various/ Various	$14.99/ TP
DC	9781401237127/ AUG120248	Red Hood and The Outlaws Vol. 1: Redemption (The New 52)	Lobdell, Scott/ Rocafort, Kenneth	$14.99/ TP
DC	9781401240905/ MAR130273	Red Hood and the Outlaws Vol. 2: The Starfire (The New 52)	Lobdell, Scott/ Rocafort, Kenneth	$14.99/ TP
DC	9781401244125/ AUG130301	Red Hood and The Outlaws Vol. 3: Death of the Family (The New 52)	Lobdell, Scott/ Green, Timothy	$16.99/ TP
DC	9781401233631/ OCT110247	Resurrection Man Vol. 1	Abnett, Dan; Lanning, Andy/ Guice, Butch	$29.99/ TP
DC	9781401235291/ MAY120284	Resurrection Man Vol. 1: Dead Again (The New 52)	Abnett, Dan; Lanning, Andy/ Dagnino, Fernando	$14.99/ TP
DC	9781401238667/ MAR130281	Resurrection Man Vol. 2: A Matter of Death and Life (The New 52)	Abnett, Dan; Lanning, Andy/ Guice, Jackson	$14.99/ TP
DC	9781401222994/ APR090212	Sandman by Kirby and Simon	Kirby, Jack/ Kirby, Jack	$39.99/ HC
DC	9781401237066/ JUL120215	The Savage Hawkman Vol. 1: Darkness Rising (The New 52)	Daniel, Tony S./ Tan, Philip	$16.99/ TP
DC	9781401240844/ SEP130277	The Savage Hawkman Vol. 2: Wanted (The New 52)	Liefeld, Rob; Poulton, Mark/ Bennett, Joe	$19.99/ TP
DC	9781401242893/ JUN130272	The Secret Society of Super-Villains Vol. 1	Various/ Various	$19.99/ TP

DC COMICS SELECTED BACKLIST

	ISBN/Diamond Code	Title	Author/Artist	US$/Format
DC	9781401231101/ JAN120312	Secret Society Super-Villains	Various/ Various	$24.99/ TP
DC	9781401231095/ APR110209	Secret Society Super-Villains Vol. 2	Levitz, Paul/ Various	$39.99/ HC
DC	9781401229511/ OCT110253	Seven Soldiers of Victory Book 1	Morrison, Grant/ Various	$29.99/ TP
DC	9781401229641/ MAR120255	Seven Soldiers of Victory Book 2	Morrison, Grant/ Various	$29.99/ TP
DC	9781401212483/ JAN070311	Sgt Rock: The Prophecy	Kubert, Joe/ Kubert, Joe	$17.99/ TP
DC	9781401238117/ NOV120267	Showcase Presents: Sgt. Rock Vol. 4	Kanigher, Robert/ Kubert, Joe	$19.99/ TP
DC	9781401237820/ NOV120272	The Shade	Robinson, James/ Various	$19.99/ TP
DC	9781401209742/ DEC080160	Shazam! and The Monster Society of Evil	Smith, Jeff/ Smith, Jeff	$19.99/ TP
DC	9781401216740/ DEC070251	Shazam! Greatest Stories Ever Told, Vol. 1	Various/ Various	$24.99/ TP
DC	9781401242442/ MAY130219	Shazam! Vol. 1 (The New 52)	Johns, Geoff/ Frank, Gary	$24.99/ HC
DC	9781401238896/ FEB130218	Solo: The Deluxe Edition	Various/ Various	$49.99/ HC
DC	9781401234188/ SEP110190	Spirit World	Kirby, Jack/ Kirby, Jack	$39.99/ HC
DC	9781401219376/ FEB120268	The Starman Omnibus Vol. 1	Robinson, James/ Harris, Tony	$29.99/ TP
DC	9781401221959/ JUN120252 T	The Starman Omnibus Vol. 2	Robinson, James/ Harris, Tony	$29.99/ TP
DC	9781401225964/ OCT090253	The Starman Omnibus Vol. 4	Robinson, James/ Harris, Tony	$49.99/ HC
DC	9781401228897/ JUN100209	The Starman Omnibus Vol. 5	Robinson, James/ Snejbjerg, Peter	$49.99/ HC
DC	9781401230449/ SEP100254	The Starman Omnibus Vol. 6	Robinson, James/ Snejbjerg, Peter	$49.99/ HC
DC	9781401234843/ MAR120245	Static Shock Vol. 1: Super-charged (The New 52)	McDaniel, Scott/ McDaniel, Scott	$16.99/ TP
DC	9781401231118/ APR110208	The Steve Ditko Omnibus Vol. 1	Various/ Ditko, Steve	$59.99/ HC
DC	9781401232351/ AUG110256	The Steve Ditko Omnibus Vol. 2	Various/ Ditko, Steve	$59.99/ HC
DC	9781401234218/ MAR130282	Stormwatch Vol. 1	Ellis, Warren/ Lee, Jim; Raney, Tom	$19.99/ TP

DC COMICS SELECTED BACKLIST

	ISBN/Diamond Code	Title	Author/Artist	US$/Format
DC	9781401237257/ FEB130219	Stormwatch Vol. 2	Ellis, Warren/ Various	$29.99/ HC
DC	9781401234836/ FEB120251	Stormwatch Vol. 1: Dark Side (The New 52)	Cornell, Paul/ Sepulveda, Miguel	$14.99/ TP
DC	9781401238483/ NOV120263	Stormwatch Vol. 2: Enemies of Earth (The New 52)	Milligan, Peter/Calero, Ignacio; Sepulveda, Miguel	$14.99/ TP
DC	9781401243159/ JUN130273	Stormwatch Vol. 3: Betrayal (The New 52)	Milligan, Peter/ Conrad, Will	$16.99/ TP
DC	9781401238469/ SEP130284	Showcase Presents: Strange Adventures Vol. 2	Various/ Various	$19.99/ TP
DC	9781401235444/ APR120250	Suicide Squad Vol. 1: Kicked In The Teeth (The New 52)	Glass, Adam/ Dallocchio, Frederico	$14.99/ TP
DC	9781401238445/ NOV120264	Suicide Squad Vol. 2: Basilisk Rising (The New 52)	Glass, Adam/ Dagnino, Fernando	$16.99/ TP
DC	9781401243166/ JUL130239	Suicide Squad Vol. 3: Death Is For Suckers (The New 52)	Glass, Adam/ Various	$14.99/ TP
DC	9781401232511/ SEP110189	Superboy Vol. 1: Smallville Attacks	Lemire, Jeff/ Gallo, Pier	$24.99/ TP
DC	9781401234850/ MAY120285	Superboy Vol. 1: Incubation (The New 52)	Lobdell, Scott/ Silva, R.B.	$14.99/ TP
DC	9781401240493/ FEB130214	Superboy Vol. 2: Extraction (The New 52)	Lobdell, Scott; Defalco, Tom/ Silva, R.B.	$14.99/ TP
DC	9781401243173/ OCT130244	Superboy Vol. 3: Lost (The New 52)	Defalco, Tom/ Silva, R.B.	$16.99/ TP
DC	9781401236809/ JUL120216	Supergirl Vol. 1: Last Daughter of Krypton (The New 52)	Green, Michael/ Asrar, Mahmud	$14.99/ TP
DC	9781401240875/ APR130223	Supergirl Vol. 2: Girl In The World (The New 52)	Green, Michael; Johnson, Mike/Asrar, Mahmud	$14.99/ TP
DC	9781401243180/ NOV130235	Supergirl Vol. 3: Sanctuary (The New 52)	Johnson, Mike/ Asrar, Mahmud	$16.99/ TP
DC	9781401234621/ MAY120280	Swamp Thing Vol. 1: Raise Them Bones (The New 52)	Snyder, Scott/ Paquette, Yanick	$14.99/ TP
DC	9781401238438/ JAN130301	Swamp Thing Vol. 2: Family Tree (The New 52)	Snyder, Scott/ Paquette, Yanick	$14.99/ TP
DC	9781401242640/ AUG130299	Swamp Thing Vol. 3: Rotworld: The Green Kingdom (The New 52)	Snyder, Scott; Lemire, Jeff/ Paquette, Yanick	$16.99/ TP
DC	9781401241001/ MAY130228	Sword of Sorcery Vol. 1: Amethyst (The New 52)	Marx, Christy/ Lopresti, Aaron	$24.99/ TP
DC	9781401238872/ MAY130217	Talon Vol. 1: Scourge of the Owls (The New 52)	Tynion IV, James; Snyder, Scott/March, Guillem	$16.99/ TP
DC	9781401240929/ APR130224	Team 7 Vol. 1: Fight Fire With Fire (The New 52)	Jordan, Justin/Meriño, Jesus	$16.99/ TP

DC COMICS SELECTED BACKLIST

	ISBN/Diamond Code	Title	Author/Artist	US$/Format
DC	9781401228095/ MAY110253	Team-Ups of the Brave and Bold	Straczynski, J. Michael/ Saiz, Jesus	$17.99/ TP
DC	9781401240882/ FEB130210	Trinity of Sin - Phantom Stranger Vol. 1: A Stranger Among Us (The New 52)	Didio, Dan/ Anderson, Brent	$14.99/ TP
DC	9781401235611/ JUN120240	Voodoo Vol. 1: What Lies Beneath (The New 52)	Marz, Ron/ Basri, Sami	$14.99/ TP
DC	9781401238155/ NOV120265	Voodoo Vol. 2: The Killer In Me (The New 52)	Williamson, Josh/ Basri, Sami	$14.99/ TP
DC	9781401238933/ MAR130265	Before Watchmen: Comedian/ Rorschach	Azzarello, Brian/ Jones, J.G.; Bermejo, Lee	$29.99/ TP
DC	9781401238926/ MAR130264	Before Watchmen: Minutemen/ Silk Spectre	Cooke, Darwyn; Conner, Amanda/ Cooke, Darwyn; Conner, Amanda	$29.99/ TP
DC	9781401238940/ MAR130266	Before Watchmen: Nite Owl/ Dr. Manhattan	Straczynski, J. Michael/ Hughes, Adam; Kubert, Andy; Kubert, Joe	$29.99/ TP
DC	9781401238957/ MAR130263	Before Watchmen: Ozymandias/ Crimson Corsair	Wein, Len/ Lee, Jae; Higgins, John	$29.99/ TP
DC	9781401238964/ FEB130225	Watchmen: The Deluxe Edition	Moore, Alan/ Gibbons, Dave	$39.99/ HC
DC	9780930289232/ JUL088045	Watchmen	Moore, Alan/ Gibbons, Dave	$19.99/ TP
DC	9781401227470/ DEC090221	Wednesday Comics	Various/ Various	$49.99/ HC
DC	9781401234775/ MAY120298	World's Finest	Gibbons, Dave/ Rude, Steve	$17.99/ TP
DC	9781401238346/ JAN130302	Worlds' Finest Vol. 1: The Lost Daughters of Earth 2 (The New 52)	Levitz, Paul/Pérez, George; McGuire, Kevin	$14.99/ TP
DC	9781401242763/ AUG130302	Worlds' Finest Vol. 2: Hunt and Be Hunted (The New 52)	Levitz, Paul/Pérez, George; McGuire, Kevin	$14.99/ TP
DC	9781401202552/ JUN100215	World's Greatest Super-Heroes	Dini, Paul/ Ross, Alex	$29.99/ TP
DC	9781401230296/ APR130241	World of Warcraft: Bloodsworn	Wagner, Doug/ Raapack, Jheremy	$24.99/ HC
DC	9781401230272/ DEC120356	World of Warcraft: Dark Riders	Costa, Michael/ Googe, Neil	$24.99/ HC
DC	9781401243968/ JUN130284	World of Warcraft: Pearl of Pandaria	Neilson, Micky/ Galloway, Sean	$16.99/ TP

VERTIGO SELECTED BACKLIST

VERTIGO	9781401224615/ JAN100348	100%	Pope, Paul/ Pope, Paul	$29.99/ TP
VERTIGO	9781563896453/ JAN128095	100 Bullets Vol. 1: First Shot, Last Call	Azzarello, Brian/ Risso, Eduardo	$9.99/ TP

VERTIGO SELECTED BACKLIST

	ISBN/Diamond Code	Title	Author/Artist	US$/Format
VERTIGO	9781563897115/ JAN128169	100 Bullets Vol. 2: Split Second Chance	Azzarello, Brian/ Risso, Eduardo	$14.99/ TP
VERTIGO	9781563898556/ OCT098206	100 Bullets Vol. 3: Hang Up On The Hang Low	Azzarello, Brian/ Risso, Eduardo	$14.99/ TP
VERTIGO	9781563898273/ JUL098295	100 Bullets Vol. 4: A Foregone Tomorrow	Azzarello, Brian/ Risso, Eduardo	$19.99/ TP
VERTIGO	9781563899485/ JUN108144	100 Bullets Vol. 5: The Counterfifth Detective	Azzarello, Brian/ Risso, Eduardo	$14.99/ TP
VERTIGO	9781563899966/ APR068251	100 Bullets Vol. 6: Six Feet Under The Gun	Azzarello, Brian/ Risso, Eduardo	$14.99/ TP
VERTIGO	9781401201890/ DEC108150	100 Bullets Vol. 7: Samurai	Azzarello, Brian/ Risso, Eduardo	$14.99/ TP
VERTIGO	9781401204907/ MAY050289	100 Bullets Vol. 8: The Hard Way	Azzarello, Brian/ Risso, Eduardo	$14.99/ TP
VERTIGO	9781401209285/ JAN060374	100 Bullets Vol. 9: Strychnine Lives	Azzarello, Brian/ Risso, Eduardo	$14.99/ TP
VERTIGO	9781401209988/ DEC118161	100 Bullets Vol. 10: Decayed	Azzarello, Brian/ Risso, Eduardo	$14.99/ TP
VERTIGO	9781401213152/ MAY070233	100 Bullets Vol. 11: Once Upon a Crime	Azzarello, Brian/ Risso, Eduardo	$12.99/ TP
VERTIGO	9781401219390/ JUN080292	100 Bullets Vol. 12: Dirty	Azzarello, Brian/ Risso, Eduardo	$12.99/ TP
VERTIGO	9781401222871/ APR090260	100 Bullets Vol. 13: Wilt	Azzarello, Brian/ Risso, Eduardo	$19.99/ TP
VERTIGO	9781401245061/ JAN140371	100 Bullets: Brother Lono	Azzarello, Brian/ Risso, Eduardo	$16.99/ TP
VERTIGO	9781401232016/ MAR110342	100 Bullets: The Deluxe Edition Book One	Azzarello, Brian/ Risso, Eduardo	$49.99/ HC
VERTIGO	9781401233723/ DEC110322	100 Bullets: The Deluxe Edition Book Two	Azzarello, Brian/ Risso, Eduardo	$49.99/ HC
VERTIGO	9781401237295/ MAY120326	100 Bullets: The Deluxe Edition Book Three	Azzarello, Brian/ Risso, Eduardo	$49.99/ HC
VERTIGO	9781401238070/ DEC120363	100 Bullets: The Deluxe Edition Book Four	Azzarello, Brian/ Risso, Eduardo	$49.99/ HC
VERTIGO	9781401242718/ JUL130265	100 Bullets: The Deluxe Edition Book Five	Azzarello, Brian/ Risso, Eduardo	$49.99/ HC
VERTIGO	9781401230890/ MAY110282	99 Days	Casali, Matteo/ Donaldson, Kristian	$19.99/ TP
VERTIGO	9781401221478/ AUG120291	A Flight of Angels	Various/ Guay, Rebecca	$17.99/ TP
VERTIGO	9781401232467/ NOV130275	A God Somewhere	Arcudi, John/ Snejbjerg, Peter	$17.99/ TP

VERTIGO SELECTED BACKLIST

	ISBN/Diamond Code	Title	Author/Artist	US$/Format
VERTIGO	9781401210816/ JUN100261	A Sickness In the Family	Mina, Denise/ Fuso, Antonio	$19.99/ HC
VERTIGO	9781401223557/ SEP110215	A.D.D.: Adolescent Demo Division	Rushkoff, Douglas/ Sudzuka, Goran	$24.99/ HC
VERTIGO	9781401221539/ DEC080208	Air Vol. 1: Letters From Lost Countries	Wilson, G. Willow/ Perker, M.K.	$9.99/ TP
VERTIGO	9781401224837/ AUG090226	Air Vol. 2: Flying Machine	Wilson, G. Willow/ Perker, M.K.	$12.99/ TP
VERTIGO	9781401227067/ FEB100248	Air Vol. 3: Pureland	Wilson, G. Willow/ Perker, M.K.	$14.99/ TP
VERTIGO	9781401229832/ NOV100267	Air Vol. 4: A History of the Future	Wilson, G. Willow/ Perker, M.K.	$14.99/ TP
VERTIGO	9781401210571/ JUN090256	The Alcoholic	Ames, Jonathan/ Haspiel, Dean	$14.99/ TP
VERTIGO	9781401212353/ JAN070366	American Splendor Vol. 1: Another Day	Pekar, Harvey/ Haspiel, Dean	$14.99/ TP
VERTIGO	9781401221737/ OCT080214	American Splendor Vol. 2: Another Dollar	Pekar, Harvey/ Lapham, David	$14.99/ TP
VERTIGO	9781401229740/ JUL110284	American Vampire Vol. 1	King, Stephen; Snyder, Scott/Albuquerque, Rafael	$19.99/ TP
VERTIGO	9781401230708/ FEB120289	American Vampire Vol. 2	Snyder, Scott/ Albuquerque, Rafael	$17.99/ TP
VERTIGO	9781401233341/ JUN120280	American Vampire Vol. 3	Snyder, Scott/ Albuquerque, Rafael	$16.99/ TP
VERTIGO	9781401237196/ JUN130293	American Vampire Vol. 4	Snyder, Scott/ Albuquerque, Rafael; Bernett, Jordi	$16.99/ TP
VERTIGO	9781401237707/ NOV120298	American Vampire Vol. 5	Snyder, Scott/ Albuquerque, Rafael; Nguyen, Dustin	$29.99/ HC
VERTIGO	9781401247089 / NOV130263	American Vampire Vol. 6	Snyder, Scott/ Albuquerque, Rafael	$22.99/ HC
VERTIGO	9781401238995/ MAR130299	The Animal Man Omnibus	Morrison, Grant/ Truog, Chas	$75.00/ HC
VERTIGO	9781563890055/ OCT068037	Animal Man Vol. 1	Morrison, Grant/ Truog, Chas	$19.99/ TP
VERTIGO	9781563898907/ JAN058098	Animal Man Vol. 2: Origin of the Species	Morrison, Grant/ Pugh, Steve	$19.99/ TP
VERTIGO	9781563899683/ JAN068276	Animal Man Vol. 3: Deus Ex Machina	Morrison, Grant/ Truog, Chas	$19.99/ TP
VERTIGO	9781401238018/ NOV120297	Animal Man Vol. 4: Born To Be Wild	Milligan, Peter/ Veitch, Tom; Dillon, Steve	$19.99/ TP
VERTIGO	9781401242848/ OCT130282	Animal Man Vol. 5: The Meaning of Flesh	Veitch, Tom/ Dillon, Steve	$14.99/ TP

VERTIGO SELECTED BACKLIST

	ISBN/Diamond Code	Title	Author/Artist	US$/Format
VERTIGO	9781401232627/ APR110229	Astro City: Life In The Big City	Busiek, Kurt/ Anderson, Brent	$17.99/ TP
VERTIGO	9781401232450/ JUL110285	Bad Doing and Big Ideas: A Bill Willingham Deluxe Edition	Willingham, Bill/ Various	$49.99/ HC
VERTIGO	9781401240202/ APR130260	Beware the Creeper	Hall, Jason/ Chiang, Cliff	$29.99/ TP
VERTIGO	9781401240356/ APR130261	Black Orchid	Gaiman, Neil/ McKean, Dave	$14.99/ TP
VERTIGO	9781401246860/ JAN140372	The Books of Magic	Gaiman, Neil/ Bolton, John	$16.99/ TP
VERTIGO	9781401226312/ DEC100291	The Bronx Kill	Milligan, Peter/ Romberger, James	$12.99/ TP
VERTIGO	9781401217341/ JUN080290	Cairo	Wilson, G. Willow/ Perker, M.K.	$17.99/ TP
VERTIGO	9781401225469/ OCT100317	The Chill	Starr, Jason/ Bertilorenzi, Mick	$12.99/ TP
VERTIGO	9781401227500/ MAY100268	Cinderella: From Fabletown with Love	Roberson, Chris/ McManus, Shawn	$14.99/ TP
VERTIGO	9781401233853/ JAN120331	Cinderella: Fables Are Forever	Roberson, Chris/ McManus, Shawn	$14.99/ TP
VERTIGO	9781401248871/ FEB140285	Coffin Hill Vol. 1	Kittredge, Caitlin/ Miranda, Inaki	$9.99/ TP
VERTIGO	9781563893438/ Star07350	Complete Moonshadow	Dematteis, J.M./ Muth, Jon J.	$39.95/ TP
VERTIGO	9781401224295/ MAY100259	Dark Entries	Rankin, Ian/ Dell'edera, Werther	$12.99/ TP
VERTIGO	9781401221614/ MAY110284	Dark Rain: A New Orleans Story	Johnson, Mat/ Gane, Simon	$19.99/ TP
VERTIGO	9781401229696/ NOV100268	Daytripper	Ba, Gabriel/ Moon, Fabio	$19.99/ TP
VERTIGO	9781401245115/ DEC130340	Daytripper Deluxe Edition	Ba, Gabriel/ Moon, Fabio	$34.99/ HC
VERTIGO	9781401234805/ FEB120290	Deadenders	Brubaker, Ed/ Bond, Philip J.	$29.99/ TP
VERTIGO	9781401247164/ DEC130341	Death	Gaiman, Neil/ Various	$19.99/ TP
VERTIGO	9781563899386/ FEB078187	Death: At Death's Door	Thompson, Jill/ Thompson, Jill	$9.99/ TP
VERTIGO	9781401224776/ NOV100264	Delirium's Party: A Little Endless Story Book	Thompson, Jill/ Thompson, Jill	$14.99/ HC
VERTIGO	9781401229955/ DEC100292	Demo Vol. 2	Wood, Brian/ Cloonan, Becky	$17.99/ TP

VERTIGO SELECTED BACKLIST

	ISBN/Diamond Code	Title	Author/Artist	US$/Format
VERTIGO	9781401241933/ JUL130269	Django Unchained	Tarantino, Quentin/ Guera, R.M.; Latour, Jason	$24.99/ HC
VERTIGO	9781401210625/ OCT118125	DMZ Vol. 1: On The Ground	Wood, Brian/ Burchielli, Riccardo	$12.99/ TP
VERTIGO	9781401212476/ JAN138241	DMZ Vol. 2: Body of A Journalist	Wood, Brian/ Burchielli, Riccardo	$14.99/ TP
VERTIGO	9781401214760/ JAN138242	DMZ Vol. 3: Public Works	Wood, Brian/ Burchielli, Riccardo	$14.99/ TP
VERTIGO	9781401216627/ DEC070294	DMZ Vol. 4: Friendly Fire	Wood, Brian/ Burchielli, Riccardo	$12.99/ TP
VERTIGO	9781401218331/ JUL108009	DMZ Vol. 5: The Hidden War	Wood, Brian/ Burchielli, Riccardo	$14.99/ TP
VERTIGO	9781401221300/ NOV080228	DMZ Vol. 6: Blood in the Game	Wood, Brian/ Burchielli, Riccardo	$12.99/ TP
VERTIGO	9781401224301/ JUN090262	DMZ Vol. 7: War Powers	Wood, Brian/ Burchielli, Riccardo	$14.99/ TP
VERTIGO	9781401227265/ APR100271	DMZ Vol. 8: Hearts and Minds	Wood, Brian/ Burchielli, Riccardo	$16.99/ TP
VERTIGO	9781401229962/ NOV100272	DMZ Vol. 9: M.I.A.	Wood, Brian/ Burchielli, Riccardo	$14.99/ TP
VERTIGO	9781401231507/ FEB110260	DMZ Vol. 10: Collective Punishment	Wood, Brian/ Burchielli, Riccardo	$14.99/ TP
VERTIGO	9781401233891/ DEC110321	DMZ Vol. 11: Free States Rising	Wood, Brian/ Burchielli, Riccardo	$19.99/ TP
VERTIGO	9781401234799/ MAR120276	DMZ Vol. 12: Five Nations of New York	Wood, Brian/ Burchielli, Riccardo	$14.99/ TP
VERTIGO	9781401243005/ SEP130306	DMZ The Deluxe Edition Book One	Wood, Brian/ Burchielli, Riccardo	$29.99/ HC
VERTIGO	9781401237424/ SEP120264	Dominique Laveau, Voodoo Child Vol. 1: Requiem	Hinds, Selwyn Seyfu/ Cowan, Denys	$14.99/ TP
VERTIGO	9781401229481/ FEB110213	Dong Xoai Vietnam 1965	Kubert, Joe/ Kubert, Joe	$19.99/ TP
VERTIGO	9781563890345/ JAN058100	Doom Patrol Vol. 1: Crawling from the Wreckage	Morrison, Grant/ Case, Richard	$19.99/ TP
VERTIGO	9781401203429/ JUL058223	Doom Patrol Vol. 2: The Painting That Ate Paris	Morrison, Grant/ Case, Richard	$19.99/ TP
VERTIGO	9781401207267/ AUG050282	Doom Patrol Vol. 3: Down Paradise Way	Morrison, Grant/ Case, Richard	$19.99/ TP
VERTIGO	9781401209995/ OCT060288	Doom Patrol Vol. 4: Musclebound	Morrison, Grant/ Case, Richard	$19.99/ TP
VERTIGO	9781401212025/ OCT060288	Doom Patrol Vol. 5: Magic Bus	Morrison, Grant/ Case, Richard	$19.99/ TP

VERTIGO SELECTED BACKLIST

	ISBN/Diamond Code	Title	Author/Artist	US$/Format
VERTIGO	9781401216245/ OCT070251	Doom Patrol Vol. 6: Planet Love	Morrison, Grant/ Case, Richard	$19.99/ TP
VERTIGO	9781401244989/ OCT130291	Ex Machina Book One	Vaughan, Brian/ K. Harris, Tony	$19.99/ TP
VERTIGO	9781401246914/ FEB140292	Ex Machina Book Two	Vaughan, Brian/ K. Harris, Tony	$19.99/ TP
VERTIGO	9781401228002/ JAN100331	Ex Machina Book Three	Vaughan, Brian/ K. Harris, Tony	$29.99/ HC
VERTIGO	9781401228453/ JUL100233	Ex Machina Book Four	Vaughan, Brian/ K. Harris, Tony	$29.99/ HC
VERTIGO	9781401229993/ DEC100280	Ex Machina Book Five	Vaughan, Brian/ K. Harris, Tony	$29.99/ HC
VERTIGO	9781401237554/ FEB120285	Fables Vol. 1: Legends In Exile	Willingham, Bill/ Buckingham, Mark	$12.99/ TP
VERTIGO	9781401200770/ MAR058123	Fables Vol. 2: Animal Farm	Willingham, Bill/ Buckingham, Mark	$14.99/ TP
VERTIGO	9781401202569/ JAN128247	Fables Vol. 3: Storybook Love	Willingham, Bill/ Buckingham, Mark	$17.99/ TP
VERTIGO	9781401202224/ OCT058021	Fables Vol. 4: March of the Wooden Soldiers	Willingham, Bill/ Buckingham, Mark	$17.99/ TP
VERTIGO	9781401204860/ JAN050373	Fables Vol. 5: The Mean Seasons	Willingham, Bill/ Buckingham, Mark	$17.99/ TP
VERTIGO	9781401205003/ OCT050317	Fables Vol. 6: Homelands	Willingham, Bill/ Buckingham, Mark	$14.99/ TP
VERTIGO	9781401210007/ MAR060384	Fables Vol. 7: Arabian Nights (and Days)	Willingham, Bill/ Buckingham, Mark	$14.99/ TP
VERTIGO	9781401210014/ SEP060313	Fables Vol. 8: Wolves	Willingham, Bill/ Buckingham, Mark	$17.99/ TP
VERTIGO	9781401213169/ MAR070271	Fables Vol. 9: Sons of Empire	Willingham, Bill/ Buckingham, Mark	$17.99/ TP
VERTIGO	9781401216863/ FEB080297	Fables Vol. 10: The Good Prince	Willingham, Bill/ Buckingham, Mark	$17.99/ TP
VERTIGO	9781401219130/ AUG080229	Fables Vol. 11: War and Pieces	Willingham, Bill/ Buckingham, Mark	$17.99/ TP
VERTIGO	9781401223168/ MAY090236	Fables Vol. 12: The Dark Ages	Willingham, Bill/ Buckingham, Mark	$17.99/ TP
VERTIGO	9781401225728/ NOV090228	Fables Vol. 13: The Great Fables Crossover	Willingham, Bill/ Buckingham, Mark	$17.99/ TP
VERTIGO	9781401228804/ SEP100304	Fables Vol. 14: Witches	Willingham, Bill/ Buckingham, Mark	$17.99/ TP
VERTIGO	9781401230005/ JAN110422	Fables Vol. 15: Rose Red	Willingham, Bill/ Buckingham, Mark	$17.99/ TP

VERTIGO SELECTED BACKLIST

	ISBN/Diamond Code	Title	Author/Artist	US$/Format
VERTIGO	9781401233068/ SEP110221	Fables Vol .16: Super Team	Willingham, Bill/ Buckingham, Mark	$14.99/ TP
VERTIGO	9781401235161/ APR120282	Fables Vol. 17: Inherit the Wind	Willingham, Bill/ Buckingham, Mark	$14.99/ TP
VERTIGO	9781401237691/ OCT120296	Fables Vol. 18: Cubs In Toyland	Willingham, Bill/ Buckingham, Mark	$16.99/ TP
VERTIGO	9781401242480/ SEP130305	Fables Vol. 19: Snow White	Willingham, Bill/ Buckingham, Mark	$16.99/ TP
VERTIGO	9781401245160/ SEP130305	Fables Vol. 20: Camelot	Willingham, Bill/ Buckingham, Mark	$19.99/ TP
VERTIGO	9781401224806/ JUL130260	Fables: Werewolves of the Heartland	Willingham, Bill/ Fern, Jim	$14.99/ TP
VERTIGO	9781401203696/ DEC070297	Fables: 1001 Nights of Snowfall	Willingham, Bill/ Various	$14.99/ TP
VERTIGO	9781401225377/ SEP100303	Peter & Max: A Fables Novel	Willingham, Bill/ Leialoha, Steve	$14.99/ TP
VERTIGO	9781401224271/ MAY090235	Fables The Deluxe Edition Book One	Willingham, Bill/ Buckingham, Mark	$29.99/ HC
VERTIGO	9781401228798/ JUL100251	Fables The Deluxe Edition Book Two	Willingham, Bill/ Buckingham, Mark	$29.99/ HC
VERTIGO	9781401230975/ APR110244	Fables The Deluxe Edition Book Three	Willingham, Bill/ Buckingham, Mark	$29.99/ HC
VERTIGO	9781401233907/ OCT110292	Fables The Deluxe Edition Book Four	Willingham, Bill/ Buckingham, Mark	$29.99/ HC
VERTIGO	9781401234966/ JAN120330	Fables The Deluxe Edition Book Five	Willingham, Bill/ Buckingham, Mark	$29.99/ HC
VERTIGO	9781401237240/ OCT120295	Fables The Deluxe Edition Book Six	Willingham, Bill/ Buckingham, Mark	$29.99/ HC
VERTIGO	9781401240400/ APR130253	Fables The Deluxe Edition Book Seven	Willingham, Bill/ Buckingham, Mark	$29.99/ HC
VERTIGO	9781401242794/ OCT130286	Fables The Deluxe Edition Book Eight	Willingham, Bill/ Buckingham, Mark	$29.99/ HC
VERTIGO	9781401243951/ JUN130286	Fables Encyclopedia	Willingham, Bill/ Various	$39.99/ HC
VERTIGO	9781401235505/ AUG120283	Fairest Vol. 1: Wide Awake	Willingham, Bill/ Jimenez, Phil	$14.99/ TP
VERTIGO	9781401240219/ APR130255	Fairest Vol. 2: Hidden Kingdom	Willingham, Bill; Beukes, Lauren/Miranda, Inaki	$14.99/ TP
VERTIGO	9781401245931/ FEB140288	Fairest Vol. 3: The Return of the Maharaja	Williams, Sean E./Sadowski, Stephen; Jimenez, Phil	$14.99/ TP
VERTIGO	9781401239008/ JUL130257	Fairest: In All the Land	Willingham, Bill/ Various	$22.99/ HC

VERTIGO SELECTED BACKLIST

	ISBN/Diamond Code	Title	Author/Artist	US$/Format
VERTIGO	9781401216634/ DEC070292	Faker	Carey, Mike/ Jock	$14.99/ TP
VERTIGO	9781401245108/ NOV130274	FBP: Federal Bureau of Physics Vol. 1: The Paradigm Shift	Oliver, Simon/ Rodriguez, Robbi	$9.99/ TP
VERTIGO	9781401200138/ APR128207	The Filth	Morrison, Grant/ Weston, Chris	$19.99/ TP
VERTIGO	9781401211851/ MAY100260	Filthy Rich	Azzarello, Brian/ Santos, Victor	$12.99/ TP
VERTIGO	9781401232214/ OCT110285	Flex Mentallo: Man of Muscle Mystery Deluxe Edition	Morrison, Grant/ Quitely, Frank	$22.99/ TP
VERTIGO	9781401200589/ AUG060290	The Fountain	Aronofsky, Darren/ Williams, Kent	$19.99/ TP
VERTIGO	9781401228286/ FEB130242	Get Jiro!	Bourdain, Anthony; Rose, Joe/Foss, Langdon	$14.99/ TP
VERTIGO	9781401242862/ JAN140369	The Girl With the Dragon Tattoo	Mina, Denise/Mutti, Andrea; Manco, Leonardo	$24.99/ TP
VERTIGO	9781401237578/ JAN140368	The Girl Who Played with Fire	Mina, Denise/Mutti, Andrea; Manco, Leonardo	$29.99/ HC
VERTIGO	9781401237974/ OCT120299	Global Frequency	Ellis, Warren/ Various	$19.99/ TP
VERTIGO	9781401223519/ NOV110226	Gone to Amerikay	McCullough, Roderick/ Doran, Colleen	$24.99/ HC
VERTIGO	9781401211011/ JUL110291	The Green Woman	Straub, Peter/ Bolton, John	$17.99/ TP
VERTIGO	9781401220075/ JUL090286	Heavy Liquid	Pope, Paul/ Pope, Paul	$24.99/ TP
VERTIGO	9781401245184/ JAN140379	Hinterkind Vol. 1	Edginton, Ian/ Trifogli, Francesco	$9.99/ TP
VERTIGO	9781401236731/ FEB130248	House of Secrets Omnibus	Seagle, Steven/ T. Kristiansen, Teddy H.	$75.00/ HC
VERTIGO	9781401222345/ JUN110354	How to Understand Israel In 60 Days Or Less	Glidden, Sarah/ Glidden, Sarah	$19.99/ TP
VERTIGO	9781401226664/ OCT090298	Human Target	Milligan, Peter/ Biukovic, Edvin	$14.99/ TP
VERTIGO	9781401230616/ NOV100270	Human Target: Second Chances	Milligan, Peter/ Pulido, Javier	$19.99/ TP
VERTIGO	9781563892677/ SEP068118	The Invisibles: Say You Want a Revolution Vol. 1	Morrison, Grant/ Yeowell, Steve	$19.99/ TP
VERTIGO	9781563897023/ OCT058209	The Invisibles: Apocalipstick Vol. 2	Morrison, Grant/ Thompson, Jill	$19.99/ TP
VERTIGO	9781563897283/ JUN058158	The Invisibles: Entropy In The U.K. Vol. 3	Morrison, Grant/ Jimenez, Phil	$19.99/ TP

VERTIGO SELECTED BACKLIST

	ISBN/Diamond Code	Title	Author/Artist	US$/Format
VERTIGO	9781563894442/ DEC118104	The Invisibles: Bloody Hell In America Vol. 4	Morrison, Grant/ Jimenez, Phil	$12.99/ TP
VERTIGO	9781563894893/ AUG058062	The Invisibles: Counting Down To None Vol. 5	Morrison, Grant/ Jimenez, Phil	$19.99/ TP
VERTIGO	9781563896002/ FEB068103	The Invisibles: Kissing Mr. Quimper Vol. 6	Morrison, Grant/ Weston, Chris	$19.99/ TP
VERTIGO	9781401200190/ JAN078237	The Invisibles: The Invisble Kingdom Vol. 7	Morrison, Grant/ Bond, Philip J.	$19.99/ TP
VERTIGO	9781401245023/ OCT130287	The Invisibles Book One Deluxe Edition	Morrison, Grant/ Various	$29.99/ HC
VERTIGO	9781401234591/ APR120288	The Invisibles Omnibus	Morrison, Grant/ Various	$150.00/ HC
VERTIGO	9781401229658/ DEC100299	Izombie Vol. 1: Dead to the World	Roberson, Chris/ Allred, Mike	$14.99/ TP
VERTIGO	9781401232962/ JUN110353	Izombie Vol. 2: Uvampire	Roberson, Chris/ Allred, Mike	$14.99/ TP
VERTIGO	9781401233709/ NOV110232	Izombie Vol. 3: Six Feet Under and Rising	Roberson, Chris/ Allred, Mike	$14.99/ TP
VERTIGO	9781401236977/ SEP120261	Izombie Vol. 4: Repossessed	Roberson, Chris/ Allred, Mike	$19.99/ TP
VERTIGO	9781401212223/ NOV060300	Jack of Fables Vol. 1: The (Nearly) Great Escape	Sturges, Matthew; Willingham, Bill/Akins, Tony	$14.99/ TP
VERTIGO	9781401214555/ JUL070305	Jack of Fables Vol. 2: Jack of Hearts	Sturges, Matthew; Willingham, Bill/Akins, Tony	$14.99/ TP
VERTIGO	9781401218546/ MAR080229	Jack of Fables Vol. 3: The Bad Prince	Sturges, Matthew; Willingham, Bill/Akins, Tony	$14.99/ TP
VERTIGO	9781401219796/ SEP080219	Jack of Fables Vol. 4: Americana	Sturges, Matthew; Willingham, Bill/Akins, Tony	$14.99/ TP
VERTIGO	9781401221386/ DEC080210	Jack of Fables Vol. 5: Turning Pages	Sturges, Matthew; Willingham, Bill/Akins, Tony	$14.99/ TP
VERTIGO	9781401225001/ JUL090281	Jack of Fables Vol. 6: The Big Book of War	Sturges, Matthew; Willingham, Bill/Akins, Tony	$14.99/ TP
VERTIGO	9781401227128/ MAR100299	Jack of Fables Vol. 7: The New Adventures of Jack and Jack	Sturges, Matthew; Willingham, Bill/Akins, Tony	$14.99/ TP
VERTIGO	9781401229825/ OCT100327	Jack of Fables Vol. 8: The Fulminate Blade	Sturges, Matthew; Willingham, Bill/Akins, Tony	$14.99/ TP
VERTIGO	9781401231552/ APR110245	Jack of Fables Vol. 9: The End	Sturges, Matthew; Willingham, Bill/Akins, Tony	$17.99/ TP
VERTIGO	9781401231798/ FEB110214	Jew Gangster	Kubert, Joe/ Kubert, Joe	$14.99/ TP
VERTIGO	9781401237479/ DEC120365	Joe the Barbarian	Morrison, Grant/ Murphy, Sean	$19.99/ TP

VERTIGO SELECTED BACKLIST

	ISBN/Diamond Code	Title	Author/Artist	US$/Format
VERTIGO	9781401230067/ DEC100302	John Constantine, Hellblazer Vol. 1: Original Sins	Delano, Jamie/ Ridgway, John	$19.99/ TP
VERTIGO	9781401233020/ SEP110218	John Constantine, Hellblazer Vol. 2: The Devil You Know	Delano, Jaime/ Lloyd, David	$19.99/ TP
VERTIGO	9781401235192/ MAR120279	John Constantine, Hellblazer Vol. 3: The Fear Machine	Delano, Jamie/ McKean, Dave	$24.99/ TP
VERTIGO	9781401236908/ AUG120288	John Constantine, Hellblazer Vol. 4: The Family Man	Various/ Lloyd, David	$19.99/ TP
VERTIGO	9781401238025/ JAN130335	John Constantine: Hellblazer Vol. 5: Dangerous Habits (New Edition)	Delano, Jamie/ Ennis, Garth	$19.99/ TP
VERTIGO	9781401240431/ MAY130258	John Constantine, Hellblazer Vol. 6: Bloodlines	Ennis, Garth/ Simpson, William	$19.99/ TP
VERTIGO	9781401243036/ OCT130283	John Constantine, Hellblazer Vol. 7: Tainted Love	Ennis, Garth/ Dillon, Steve	$19.99/ TP
VERTIGO	9781563899713/ Star18495	John Constantine, Hellblazer: Freezes Over	Azzarello, Brian/ Bradstreet, Tim	$14.95/ TP
VERTIGO	9781401210038/ JAN060378	John Constantine, Hellblazer: Papa Midnite	Johnson, Mat/ Akins, Tony	$12.99/ TP
VERTIGO	9781401214531/ JUN070273	John Constantine, Hellblazer: The Gift	Carey, Mike/ Manco, Leonardo	$14.99/ TP
VERTIGO	9781401204853/ MAR050480	John Constantine, Hellblazer: Red Sepulchre	Carey, Mike/ Dillon, Steve	$12.99/ TP
VERTIGO	9781401203177/ APR060290	John Constantine, Hellblazer: All His Engines	Carey, Mike/ Manco, Leonardo	$14.99/ TP
VERTIGO	9781401210021/ MAY060237	John Constantine, Hellblazer: Stations of the Cross	Carey, Mike/ Bradstreet, Tim	$14.99/ TP
VERTIGO	9781401216511/ NOV070297	John Constantine, Hellblazer: Joyride	Diggle, Andy/ Manco, Leonardo	$14.99/ TP
VERTIGO	9781401220396/ NOV100274	John Constantine, Hellblazer: Pandemonium	Delano, Jamie/ Jock	$17.99/ TP
VERTIGO	9781401225018/ AUG090230	John Constantine, Hellblazer: Scab	Milligan, Peter/ Camuncoli, Giuseppe	$14.99/ TP
VERTIGO	9781401231521/ APR110249	John Constantine, Hellblazer: Bloody Carnations	Milligan, Peter/ Camuncoli, Giuseppe	$19.99/ TP
VERTIGO	9781401233990/ NOV110228	John Constantine, Hellblazer: Phantom Pains	Milligan, Peter/ Camuncoli, Giuseppe	$14.99/ TP
VERTIGO	9781401237202/ JUL120255	John Constantine, Hellblazer: The Devil's Trenchcoat	Milligan, Peter/ Camuncoli, Giuseppe	$16.99/ TP
VERTIGO	9781401240936/ MAR130304	John Constantine, Hellblazer: Death and Cigarettes	Milligan, Peter/ Camuncoli, Giuseppe; Bisley, Simon	$19.99/ TP
VERTIGO	9781563898587/ MAY118167	The League of Extraordinary Gentlemen Vol. 1	Moore, Alan/ O'Neill, Kevin	$16.99/ TP

VERTIGO SELECTED BACKLIST

	ISBN/Diamond Code	Title	Author/Artist	US$/Format
VERTIGO	9781401201180/ MAY118168	The League of Extraordinary Gentlemen Vol. 2	Moore, Alan/ O'Neill, Kevin	$16.99/ TP
VERTIGO	9781401203078/ JUL080193	The League of Extraordinary Gentlemen: Black Dossier	Moore, Alan/ O'Neill, Kevin	$19.99/ TP
VERTIGO	9781401240837/ MAY130257	The League of Extraordinary Gentlemen Omnibus	Moore, Alan/ O'Neill, Kevin	$29.99/ TP
VERTIGO	9781401204280/ NOV100265	The Little Endless Storybook	Thompson, Jill/ Thompson, Jill	$14.99/ TP
VERTIGO	9781401227333/ NOV090232	The Losers Book One	Diggle, Andy/ Jock	$19.99/ TP
VERTIGO	9781401229238/ MAY100275	The Losers Book Two	Diggle, Andy/ Jock	$24.99/ TP
VERTIGO	9781401240264/ FEB130247	Lucifer Book One	Carey, Mike/ Gross, Peter; Hampton, Scott	$29.99/ TP
VERTIGO	9781401242602/ JUL130266	Lucifer Book Two	Carey, Mike/ Gross, Peter	$29.99/ TP
VERTIGO	9781401229597/ JUL110278	Marzi	Sowa, Marzena/ Savoia, Sylvain	$17.99/ TP
VERTIGO	9781563892462/ SEP058283	Mr. Punch	Gaiman, Neil/ McKean, Dave	$19.99/ TP
VERTIGO	9781563891892/ Star18959	Mystery Play	Morrison, Grant/ Muth, Jon J	$12.95/ TP
VERTIGO	9781401234577/ MAR120280	Neil Gaiman's Midnight Days Deluxe Edition	Gaiman, Neil/ McKean, Dave	$24.99/ HC
VERTIGO	9781401210076/ NOV060304	Neil Gaiman's Neverwhere	Carey, Mike/ Fabry, Glenn	$19.99/ TP
VERTIGO	9781401228224/ JUN130298	Neil Young's Greendale	Dysart, Josh/ Chiang, Cliff	$14.99/ TP
VERTIGO	9781401237639/ NOV120301	The New Deadwardians	Abnett, Dan/ Culbard, I.N.J.	$14.99/ TP
VERTIGO	9781401211547/ APR080265	The New York Four	Wood, Brian/ Kelly, Ryan	$9.99/ TP
VERTIGO	9781401232917/ JUN110351	The New York Five	Wood, Brian/ Kelly, Ryan	$14.99/ TP
VERTIGO	9781401202682/ JUL088085	Orbiter	Ellis, Warren/ Doran, Colleen	$17.99/ TP
VERTIGO	9781401203566/ AUG050289	The Originals	Gibbons, Dave/ Gibbons, Dave	$17.99/ TP
VERTIGO	9781401215354/ OCT100316	Noche Roja	Oliver, Simon/ Latour, Jason	$19.99/ HC
VERTIGO	9781401240455/ MAR130303	Preacher Book One	Ennis, Garth/ Dillon, Steve	$19.99/ TP

VERTIGO SELECTED BACKLIST

	ISBN/Diamond Code	Title	Author/Artist	US$/Format
VERTIGO	9781401242558/ JUN130299	Preacher Book Two	Ennis, Garth/ Dillon, Steve	$19.99/ TP
VERTIGO	9781401245016/ OCT130293	Preacher Book Three	Ennis, Garth/ Dillon, Steve	$19.99/ TP
VERTIGO	9781401230937/ FEB110265	Preacher Book Four	Ennis, Garth/ Dillon, Steve	$39.99/ HC
VERTIGO	9781401234157/ SEP110226	Preacher Book Six	Ennis, Garth/ Dillon, Steve	$39.99/ HC
VERTIGO	9781563893124/ JUL118011	Preacher Vol. 2: Until The End of the World	Ennis, Garth/ Dillon, Steve	$17.99/ TP
VERTIGO	9781563893278/ MAY138356	Preacher Vol. 3: Proud Americans	Ennis, Garth/ Dillon, Steve	$16.99/ TP
VERTIGO	9781563894053/ FEB118118	Preacher Vol. 4: Ancient History	Ennis, Garth/ Dillon, Steve	$17.99/ TP
VERTIGO	9781563894282/ JUL128119	Preacher Vol. 5: Dixie Fried	Ennis, Garth/ Dillon, Steve	$14.99/ TP
VERTIGO	9781563894909/ MAY050301	Preacher Vol. 6: War In The Sun	Ennis, Garth/ Dillon, Steve	$17.99/ TP
VERTIGO	9781563895197/ MAY050300	Preacher Vol. 7: Salvation	Ennis, Garth/ Dillon, Steve	$17.99/ TP
VERTIGO	9781563896170/ SEP058101	Preacher Vol. 8: All Hell's A-Coming	Ennis, Garth/ Dillon, Steve	$17.99/ TP
VERTIGO	9781563897153/ APR078094	Preacher Vol. 9: Alamo	Ennis, Garth/ Dillon, Steve	$17.99/ TP
VERTIGO	9781401203153/ FEB118119	Pride of Baghdad	Vaughan, Brian K./ Henrichon, Niko	$14.99/ TP
VERTIGO	9781563896675/ APR108106	Promethea Book 1	Moore, Alan/Williams III, J.H.	$17.99/ TP
VERTIGO	9781401200947/ AUG128046	Promethea Book 2	Moore, Alan/ Williams III, J.H.	$17.99/ TP
VERTIGO	9781563896675/ AUG128047	Promethea Book 3	Moore, Alan/ Williams III, J.H.	$17.99/ TP
VERTIGO	9781401200312/ OCT098137	Promethea Book 4	Moore, Alan/ Williams III, J.H.	$17.99/ TP
VERTIGO	9781401206208/ MAY060224	Promethea Book 5	Moore, Alan/ Williams III, J.H.	$14.99/ TP
VERTIGO	9781401237684/ JAN130330	Punk Rock Jesus	Murphy, Sean/ Murphy, Sean	$16.99/ TP
VERTIGO	9781401211585/ SEP100300	Rat Catcher	Diggle, Andy/ Ibanez, Victor	$19.99/ TP
VERTIGO	9781401222420/ APR110251	Revolver	Kindt, Matt/ Kindt, Matt	$19.99/ TP

VERTIGO SELECTED BACKLIST

	ISBN/Diamond Code	Title	Author/Artist	US$/Format
VERTIGO	9781401229443/ MAY130262	Right State	Johnson, Mat/ Mutti, Andrea	$16.99/ TP
VERTIGO	9781401231910/ JUL110280	Road To Perdition	Collins, Max/ Allan Rayner, Richard Piers	$14.99/ TP
VERTIGO	9781401231903/ JUL110281	Road To Perdition 2: On The Road	Collins, Max Allan/ Garcia-Lopez, Jose Luis	$14.99/ TP
VERTIGO	9781401223847/ AUG120296	Return To Perdition	Collins, Max/ Allan Beatty, Terry	$14.99/ TP
VERTIGO	9781401220839/ JAN120343	Saga of the Swamp Thing Book One	Moore, Alan/ Various	$19.99/ TP
VERTIGO	9781401225445/ JUN120283	Saga of the Swamp Thing Book Two	Moore, Alan/ Various	$19.99/ TP
VERTIGO	9781401227678/ OCT120301	Saga of the Swamp Thing Book Three	Moore, Alan/ Bissette, Steve	$19.99/ TP
VERTIGO	9781401240462/ APR130262	Saga of the Swamp Thing Book Four	Moore, Alan/Bissette, Stephen, Woch, Stan	$19.99/ TP
VERTIGO	9781401230968/ SEP130310	Saga of the Swamp Thing Book Five	Moore, Alan/ Veitch, Rick	$14.99/ TP
VERTIGO	9781401232986/ JUN110356	Saga of the Swamp Thing Book Six	Moore, Alan/ Totleben, John	$24.99/ HC
VERTIGO	9781401243043/ OCT130292	Swamp Thing by Brian K. Vaughan Vol. 1	Vaughan, Brian K./Peterson, Roger; Chiang, Cliff	$19.99/ TP
VERTIGO	9781401241889/ APR130263	The Sandman Omnibus Vol. 1	Gaiman, Neil/ Various	$150.00/ HC
VERTIGO	9781401243142/ JUL130263	The Sandman Omnibus Vol. 2	Gaiman, Neil/ Various	$150.00/ HC
VERTIGO	9781401225759/ JUL100259	The Sandman Vol. 1: Preludes & Nocturnes	Gaiman, Neil/Kieth, Sam	$19.99/ TP
VERTIGO	9781401227999/ JUL100260	The Sandman Vol. 2: The Doll's House	Gaiman, Neil/ Dringenberg, Mike	$19.99/ TP
VERTIGO	9781401229351/ JUL100261	The Sandman Vol. 3: Dream Country	Gaiman, Neil/ Jones, Kelley	$19.99/ TP
VERTIGO	9781401230425/ OCT100330	The Sandman Vol. 4: Season of Mists	Gaiman, Neil/ Jones, Kelley	$19.99/ TP
VERTIGO	9781401230432/ JAN110431	The Sandman Vol. 5: A Game of You	Gaiman, Neil/ McManus, Shawn	$19.99/ TP
VERTIGO	9781401231231/ MAY110297	The Sandman Vol. 6: Fables & Reflections	Gaiman, Neil/ Talbot, Bryan	$19.99/ TP
VERTIGO	9781401232634/ SEP110177	The Sandman Vol. 7: Brief Lives	Gaiman, Neil/ Thompson, Jill	$19.99/ TP
VERTIGO	9781401234027/ NOV110233	The Sandman Vol. 8: Worlds' End	Gaiman, Neil/ Allred, Mike	$19.99/ TP

VERTIGO SELECTED BACKLIST

	ISBN/Diamond Code	Title	Author/Artist	US$/Format
VERTIGO	9781401235451/ FEB120298	The Sandman Vol. 9: The Kindly Ones	Gaiman, Neil/ Hempel, Marc	$19.99/ TP
VERTIGO	9781401237547/ AUG120292	The Sandman Vol. 10: The Wake	Gaiman, Neil/ Zulli, Michael	$19.99/ TP
VERTIGO	9781563896293/ DEC068030	The Sandman: The Dream Hunters	Gaiman, Neil/ Amano, Yoshitaka	$19.99/ TP
VERTIGO	9781401224288/ JUN100280	The Sandman: The Dream Hunters	Gaiman, Neil/ Russell, P. Craig	$19.99/ TP
VERTIGO	9781401242336/ JUL130264	The Sandman: Endless Nights	Gaiman, Neil/ Various	$19.99/ TP
VERTIGO	9781563893872/ Star07911	The Sandman: The Collected Dustcovers	McKean, Dave/ McKean, Dave	$24.95/ TP
VERTIGO	9781401233327/ AUG110277	The Annotated Sandman Vol. 1	Gaiman, Neil/ Various	$49.99/ HC
VERTIGO	9781401235666/ JUN120271	The Annotated Sandman Vol. 2	Gaiman, Neil/ Various	$49.99/ HC
VERTIGO	9781401204976/ JUN050447	The Sandman Presents: Thessaly - Witch For Hire	Willingham, Bill/ McManus, Shawn	$12.99/ TP
VERTIGO	9781401218553/ MAY080258	The Sandman Presents: Dead Boy Detectives	Brubaker, Ed/ Talbot, Bryan	$12.99/ TP
VERTIGO	9781401235499/ AUG120295	Saucer Country Vol. 1: Run	Cornell, Paul/ Kelly, Ryan	$14.99/ TP
VERTIGO	9781401240479/ MAY130259	Saucer Country Vol. 2: The Reticulan Candidate	Cornell, Paul/Broxton, Jimmy; Lapham, David	$16.99/ TP
VERTIGO	9781401213176/ APR108251	Scalped Vol. 1: Indian Country	Aaron, Jason/ Guera, R.M.	$14.99/ TP
VERTIGO	9781401216542/ NOV070301	Scalped Vol. 2: Casino Boogie	Aaron, Jason/ Guera, R.M.	$14.99/ TP
VERTIGO	9781401219192/ JUN080304	Scalped Vol. 3: Dead Mothers	Aaron, Jason/ Guera, R.M.	$17.99/ TP
VERTIGO	9781401221799/ JAN090288	Scalped Vol. 4: The Gravel In Your Guts	Aaron, Jason/ Guera, R.M.	$14.99/ TP
VERTIGO	9781401224875/ JUL090293	Scalped Vol. 5: High Lonesome	Aaron, Jason/ Guera, R.M.	$14.99/ TP
VERTIGO	9781401227173/ FEB100266	Scalped Vol. 6: The Gnawing	Aaron, Jason/ Guera, R.M.	$14.99/ TP
VERTIGO	9781401230197/ NOV100278	Scalped Vol. 7: Rez Blues	Aaron, Jason/ Guera, R.M.	$17.99/ TP
VERTIGO	9781401232887/ AUG110288	Scalped Vol. 8: You Gotta Sin To Get Saved	Aaron, Jason/ Guera, R.M.	$17.99/ TP
VERTIGO	9781401235055/ APR120293	Scalped Vol. 9: Knuckle Up	Aaron, Jason/ Guera, R.M.	$14.99/ TP

VERTIGO SELECTED BACKLIST

	ISBN/Diamond Code	Title	Author/Artist	US$/Format
VERTIGO	9781401237349/ JUL120253	Scalped Vol. 10: Trail's End	Aaron, Jason/ Guera, R.M.	$14.99/ TP
VERTIGO	9781401200466/ AUG090239	Shade, The Changing Man Vol. 1: American Scream	Milligan, Peter/ Bachalo, Chris	$17.99/ TP
VERTIGO	9781401225391/ AUG090240	Shade, The Changing Man Vol. 2: Edge of Vision	Milligan, Peter/ Bachalo, Chris	$19.99/ TP
VERTIGO	9781401227685/ MAR100311	Shade, The Changing Man Vol. 3: Scream Time	Milligan, Peter/ Hewlett, Jamie	$19.99/ TP
VERTIGO	9781401222154/ DEC110314	Shooters	Jerwa, Brandon/ Lieber, Steven	$22.99/ HC
VERTIGO	9781401223601/ MAR090210	Sleeper: Season One	Brubaker, Ed/ Phillips, Sean	$24.99/ TP
VERTIGO	9781401224936/ JUN090248	Sleeper: Season Two	Brubaker, Ed/ Phillips, Sean	$24.99/ TP
VERTIGO	9781401238032/ OCT120298	The Sleeper Omnibus	Brubaker, Ed/ Phillips, Sean	$75.00/ HC
VERTIGO	9781401242701/ NOV130269	Spaceman	Azzarello, Brian/ Risso, Eduardo	$19.99/ TP
VERTIGO	9781563894701/ FEB058028	Stardust	Gaiman, Neil/ Vess, Charlie	$19.99/ TP
VERTIGO	9781401243937/ NOV130276	Strange Adventures	Various/ Various	$14.99/ TP
VERTIGO	9781401226961/ AUG108007	Sweet Tooth Vol. 1: Out of the Deep Woods	Lemire, Jeff/ Lemire, Jeff	$12.99/ TP
VERTIGO	9781401228545/ OCT118099	Sweet Tooth Vol. 2: In Captivity	Lemire, Jeff/ Lemire, Jeff	$12.99/ TP
VERTIGO	9781401231705/ MAR110392	Sweet Tooth Vol. 3: Animal Armies	Lemire, Jeff/ Lemire, Jeff	$14.99/ TP
VERTIGO	9781401233617/ OCT110296	Sweet Tooth Vol. 4: Endangered Species	Lemire, Jeff/ Lemire, Jeff	$16.99/ TP
VERTIGO	9781401237233/ JUL120259	Sweet Tooth Vol. 5: Unnatural Habit	Lemire, Jeff/ Lemire, Jeff	$14.99 / TP
VERTIGO	9781401240295/ MAR130305	Sweet Tooth Vol. 6: Wild Game	Lemire, Jeff/ Lemire, Jeff	$16.99/ TP
VERTIGO	9781401242800/ OCT130294	Terra Obscura: S.M.A.S.H. of Two Worlds	Moore, Alan; Hogan, Peter/ Paquette, Yanick	$24.99/ TP
VERTIGO	9781401225360/ MAY090229	Tom Strong Deluxe Vol. 1	Moore, Alan/ Sprouse, Chris	$39.99/ HC
VERTIGO	9781401226800/ DEC090253	Tom Strong Deluxe Vol. 2	Moore, Alan/ Sprouse, Chris	$39.99/ HC
VERTIGO	9781401238254/ SEP120255	Absolute Top 10	Moore, Alan/ Ha, Gene	$99.99/ HC

VERTIGO SELECTED BACKLIST

	ISBN/Diamond Code	Title	Author/Artist	US$/Format
VERTIGO	9781401205737/ JAN060370	Top Ten: The Forty Niners	Moore, Alan/ Ha, Gene	$17.99/ TP
VERTIGO	9781401220846/ DEC080220	Transmetropolitan Vol. 1: Back On The Street	Ellis, Warren/ Robertson, Darick	$14.99/ TP
VERTIGO	9781401222611/ FEB090264	Transmetropolitan Vol. 2: Lust For Life	Ellis, Warren/ Robertson, Darick	$14.99/ TP
VERTIGO	9781401223120/ DEC098262	Transmetropolitan Vol. 3: Year of the Bastard	Ellis, Warren/ Robertson, Darick	$14.99/ TP
VERTIGO	9781401224905/ JUL090291	Transmetropolitan Vol. 4: The New Scum	Ellis, Warren/ Robertson, Darick	$14.99/ TP
VERTIGO	9781401228194/ SEP090228	Transmetropolitan Vol. 5: Lonely City	Ellis, Warren/ Robertson, Darick	$14.99/ TP
VERTIGO	9781401228187/ DEC090284	Transmetropolitan Vol. 6: Gouge Away	Ellis, Warren/ Robertson, Darick	$14.99/ TP
VERTIGO	9781401228156/ FEB100264	Transmetropolitan Vol. 7: Spider's Thrash	Ellis, Warren/ Robertson, Darick	$14.99/ TP
VERTIGO	9781401229368/ JUN100282	Transmetropolitan Vol. 8: Dirge	Ellis, Warren/ Robertson, Darick	$14.99/ TP
VERTIGO	9781401230494/ JAN110435	Transmetropolitan Vol. 9: The Cure	Ellis, Warren/ Robertson, Darick	$14.99/ TP
VERTIGO	9781401231248/ MAY110296	Transmetropolitan Vol. 10: One More Time	Ellis, Warren/ Robertson, Darick	$19.99/ TP
VERTIGO	9781401243944/ JUL130271	The Unexpected	Various/ Various	$14.99/ TP
VERTIGO	9781401223113/ MAY090251	Unknown Soldier Vol. 1: Haunted House	Dysart, Joshua/ Ponticelli, Alberto	$9.99/ TP
VERTIGO	9781401226008/ DEC090283	Unknown Soldier Vol. 2: Easy Kill	Dysart, Joshua/ Ponticelli, Alberto	$17.99/ TP
VERTIGO	9781401228552/ AUG100276	Unknown Soldier Vol. 3: Dry Season	Dysart, Joshua/ Ponticelli, Alberto	$14.99/ TP
VERTIGO	9781401231767/ FEB110269	Unknown Soldier Vol. 4: Beautiful World	Dysart, Joshua/ Ponticelli, Alberto	$14.99/ TP
VERTIGO	9781401225650/ APR128238	The Unwritten Vol. 1: Tommy Taylor and The Bogus Identity	Carey, Mike/ Gross, Peter	$12.99/ TP
VERTIGO	9781401228736/ MAY100283	The Unwritten Vol. 2: Inside Man	Carey, Mike/ Gross, Peter	$12.99/ TP
VERTIGO	9781401230463/ DEC100305	The Unwritten Vol. 3: Dead Man's Knock	Carey, Mike/ Gross, Peter	$14.99/ TP
VERTIGO	9781401232924/ JUL110296	The Unwritten Vol. 4: Leviathan	Carey, Mike/ Gross, Peter	$14.99/ TP
VERTIGO	9781401233594/ OCT110301	The Unwritten Vol. 5: On To Genesis	Carey, Mike/ Gross, Peter	$14.99/ TP

VERTIGO SELECTED BACKLIST

	ISBN/Diamond Code	Title	Author/Artist	US$/Format
VERTIGO	9781401235604/ JUL120262	The Unwritten Vol. 6: Tommy Taylor and the War of Words	Carey, Mike/ Gross, Peter	$16.99/ TP
VERTIGO	9781401238063/ DEC120368	The Unwritten Vol. 7: The Wound	Carey, Mike/ Gross, Peter	$14.99/ TP
VERTIGO	9781401243012/ OCT130295	The Unwritten Vol. 8: Orpheus In the Underworlds	Carey, Mike/ Gross, Peter	$16.99/ TP
VERTIGO	9781401229764/ MAY130251	The Unwritten: Tommy Taylor and The Ship That Sank Twice	Carey, Mike/ Gross, Peter	$22.99/ HC
VERTIGO	9781401208417/ SEP088030	V For Vendetta	Moore, Alan/ Lloyd, David	$19.99/ TP
VERTIGO	9781401243029	We3	Morrison, Grant/ Quitely, Frank	$14.99/ TP
VERTIGO	9781563899805/ DEC108152	Y: The Last Man Vol. 1: Unmanned	Vaughan, Brian K./ Guerra, Pia	$14.99/ TP
VERTIGO	9781401200763/ OCT058281	Y: The Last Man Vol. 2: Cycles	Vaughan, Brian K./ Guerra, Pia	$12.99/ TP
VERTIGO	9781401202019/ FEB118093	Y: The Last Man Vol. 3: One Small Step	Vaughan, Brian K./ Guerra, Pia	$14.99/ TP
VERTIGO	9781401202323/ DEC108199	Y: The Last Man Vol. 4: Safeword	Vaughan, Brian K./ Guerra, Pia	$12.99/ TP
VERTIGO	9781401204877/ MAY050306	Y: The Last Man Vol. 5: Ring of Truth	Vaughan, Brian K./ Guerra, Pia	$14.99/ TP
VERTIGO	9781401205010/ DEC108151	Y: The Last Man Vol. 6: Girl On Girl	Vaughan, Brian K./ Guerra, Pia	$14.99/ TP
VERTIGO	9781401210090/ FEB060341	Y: The Last Man Vol. 7: Paper Dolls	Vaughan, Brian K./ Guerra, Pia	$14.99/ TP
VERTIGO	9781401210106/ AUG060299	Y: The Last Man Vol. 8: Kimono Dragons	Vaughan, Brian K./ Guerra, Pia	$14.99/ TP
VERTIGO	9781401213510/ FEB070362	Y: The Last Man Vol. 9: Motherland	Vaughan, Brian K./ Guerra, Pia	$14.99/ TP
VERTIGO	9781401218133/ MAR080241	Y: The Last Man Vol 10: Whys and Wherefores	Vaughan, Brian K./ Guerra, Pia	$14.99/ TP
VERTIGO	9781401219215/ JUN080308	Y: The Last Man Deluxe Book 1	Vaughan, Brian K./ Guerra, Pia	$29.99/ HC
VERTIGO	9781401222352/ JAN090291	Y: The Last Man Deluxe Book 2	Vaughan, Brian K./ Guerra, Pia	$29.99/ HC
VERTIGO	9781401225780/ DEC090285	Y: The Last Man Deluxe Book 3	Vaughan, Brian K./ Guerra, Pia	$29.99/ HC
VERTIGO	9781401228880/ JUN100278	Y: The Last Man Deluxe Book 4	Vaughan, Brian K./ Guerra, Pia	$29.99/ HC
VERTIGO	9781401230517/ DEC100308	Y: The Last Man Deluxe Book 5	Vaughan, Brian K./ Guerra, Pia	$29.99/ HC

ORDER INFORMATION

BOOK TRADE

DC Entertainment titles are distributed to the book trade by Random House Publishers Services and are eligible for cooperative advertising and free freight. Please contact the Random House sales representative in your region.

UNITED STATES

Random House Customer Service
400 Hahn Road
Westminster, MD 21157
To order by phone or for customer service:
1-800-733-3000
Available daily 8:30AM to 5:00PM EST
(Eastern and Central Accounts)
10:30AM to 7:00PM EST
(Western Accounts)
Fax: 1-800-659-2436
csorders@randomhouse.com

Visit the website at www.randomhouse.com. You can place an order, check on an order, file claims, check title availability; request invoice copies and much more.

ELECTRONIC ORDERING (EDI):
1-800-726-0600
Minimum orders:
Initials: $100 retail value
Reorders: $200 retail value

SCHOOLS AND LIBRARIES
The Library and Academic Marketing Department is available to provide title information, review copies, desk and examination copies, and any other educational materials.

For Libraries, visit www.randomhouse.com/library or email: library@randomhouse.com

For High Schools, visit www.randomhouse.com/highschool or email: highschool@randomhouse.com

For Colleges and Universities, visit www.randomhouse.com/academic or email: RHAcademic@randomhouse.com

SPECIAL MARKETS
Random House Special Markets
1745 Broadway
New York, NY 10019
Website: www.randomhouse.biz/specialmarkets
Email: specialmarkets@randomhouse.com
Fax: 212-572-4961

CANADA

Random House of Canada Limited
2775 Matheson Boulevard East
Mississauga, Ontario L4W4P7
To order by phone or for customer service:
1-888-523-9292
8:30AM to 5:00PM EST (Monday through Friday)
Canadian Telebook I.D. S2013975
Fax ordering: 1-888-562-9924
Shipping Minimum (Reorders and New title): $100
Retail notice to all Canadian customers:
Suggested Canadian list prices do not include the Federal Goods and Services Tax (GST)

Returns: Random House of Canada, Ltd.
2775 Matheson Boulevard East
Mississauga, Ontario L4W 4P7

INTERNATIONAL

Random House, Inc. International Department
1745 Broadway
New York, NY 10019
1-212-829-6712
Fax: 1-212-572-6045; 1-212-829-6700
Email: international@randomhouse.com
Minimum order: $100 retail value

UNITED KINGDOM

Diamond Book Distributors UK
Canalside, Warrington Road
Manor Park, Runcorn
Cheshire WA7 1SN
Tel: 0044 (0) 1928 531760
Email: orders@diamondcomics.co.uk

Simon Byrne, Sales Manager
Mobile: 0044 (0) 7951 332815

Andrew Whelan, Sales Manager
Mobile: 0044 (0) 7710071102

DIRECT MARKET

Diamond Book Distributors
reorders@diamondcomics.com
(800) 45-COMIC

Friend us on 

Follow us on 

VISIT US AT DCCOMICS.COM & VERTIGOCOMICS.COM